Earth Sciences series

Front cover image: The Forth Railway Bridge, constructed in 1885 using stone pillars of Kemnay granite from Aberdeenshire and sandstone (Arbroath stone) from the Carmyllie quarries in Angus. In the foreground Carboniferous sandstone of the West Lothian Oil-Shale Formation, which has produced some of the finest building stone in Scotland. BGS © NERC. Photo: A. McMillan.

Back cover image: The new Scottish Parliament building in Edinburgh, completed 2004, partially clad in silver-grey granite from Kemnay quarry in Aberdeenshire. BGS © NERC Photo: E. Hyslop.

Published in 2006 by the United Nations Educational, Scientific and Cultural Organization 7, place de Fontenoy, 75007 Paris, France, and the International Association of Engineering Geology (IAEG), The Crown, the British Geological Survey and the Natural Environment Research Council.

Typeset by Gérard Prosper
Printed by Sagrafic, Barcelona

ISBN-10: 92-3-104031-6
ISBN-13: 978-92-3-104031-3

Printed in Spain

Stone in Scotland

Authors

Ewan Hyslop, B.Sc., M.Sc., Ph.D., CGeol, FGS (British Geological Survey)

Andrew McMillan, B.Sc., CGeol, FGS (British Geological Survey)

Ingval Maxwell, OBE, DADun, RIBA, FRIAS, AABC, FSAScot (Historic Scotland)

Contributors

Joan Walsh, B.Sc., Ph.D., PGCE (University of Paisley)

Luis Albornoz-Parra, B.Sc. (British Geological Survey)

Earth Sciences series

UNESCO Publishing • IAEG • Queen's Printer for Scotland •
The British Geological Survey and Natural Environment Research Council

Acknowledgements

This publication was made possible through the collaboration of the British Geological Survey and Historic Scotland with the support of the International Association of Engineering Geology and UNESCO.

The authors wish to thank Asher Shadmon (IAEG) for initiating this project and editorial and general support, Eileen Callaghan and Joyce Bain (BGS) for compiling the maps, and Dr Graham Lott (BGS) for reviewing the manuscript. Photographs in Annex I were taken by Fergus MacTaggart (BGS).

Foreword

It is coincidental that the publication of the present book takes place during the sixtieth anniversary of UNESCO at a time when global developments are viewed in an environmental context. Scotland's attention to the link of heritage to environment is arguably one of the largest contributions of its kind when considering the size of its population, and has received wide international recognition. Furthermore it is also the year when the 10th International Congress of IAEG has chosen as its theme 'Engineering Geology for Tomorrow's Cities' in Nottingham, UK and to discuss the visual and geotechnical impacts of environmental change on engineering construction.

Co-operation between UNESCO and IAEG actually dates back to the mid-1960s with IAEG holding its 1st IAEG Congress at UNESCO in Paris in 1970 and resulted in the first joint in-house-publication of the 'UNESCO-IAEG Engineering Geological Maps-Guide to their Preparation' in 1976.

Activities of UNESCO and IAEG during the UN Decade on Natural Disaster Reduction (1989–1999), to serve the global community with research, information and training in 'geo-factors' by its affiliated commissions, is another example of the ongoing co-operation and has been put in focus by the recent geohazards in SE Asia, the southern USA and elsewhere.

The support UNESCO lent to the publication of the books Stone in Southern Africa (1999) and Nordic Stone (2003), and now Stone in Scotland demonstrates the importance the Organization gives to geosciences in the planning processes for resources development, to sustainably manage widely available common earth materials for the benefit of society. The integration of a social dimension into the Earth Sciences is further demonstrated by the support UNESCO gives to the implementation of the Global Earth Observing Section of Systems over the period 2005–2015, and the proclamation by the United Nations of the year 2008 as the International Year of the Planet Earth – Earth Sciences for Society.

UNESCO would like to express its appreciation for the cooperation with IAEG, Historic Scotland and the British Geological Survey for the preparation of the present publication and, in particular, we would like to thank Asher Shadmon for his continuing support for the preparation of the Stone in the World Series, highlighting the outstanding contribution the Earth Sciences can make to society.

Robert Missotten
Chief, UNESCO Global Earth Observation Section

Stone in Scotland – ISBN 978-92-3-104031-3 – © UNESCO 2006

Contents

Stone in Scotland – ISBN 978-92-3-104031-3 – © UNESCO 2006

Preface

Stone in Scotland follows previous monographs on stone produced by various United Nations agencies covering several countries and regions and presently co-published by UNESCO IAEG C-10 as part of the Geological Science Series.

Globalization has resulted in a dramatic increase in stone resources hitherto used indigenously. Information on these resources is well behind demand. These monographs have been designed to fill this gap, their major objective being to supply and share knowledge at both local and international levels.

It is not that the geological richness of Scotland is 'wasting its sweetness in the desert air'; the stone resources of Scotland have been well-recorded and the rock types included in teaching curricula. The recommended reading of Hugh Miller's The Old Red Sandstone during college days generously compensated for long, dark winter afternoons whiled away scanning petrographical slides of Lion's Haunch 'type' olivine basalt through a microscope. These conjured up images of Edinburgh lions, until a visit to the hill decades later banished the illusions of a budding geologist.

The information in this publication is contributed by eminent specialists with an interest in the related environmental and heritage issues. It is, in particular, the issue of heritage that underlines Scotland's importance for this series of country-based monographs. Numerous publications by Historic Scotland's Technical, Conservation, Research and Education Group have established an enviable reputation within the international fraternity of restorers, conservationists and allied disciplines.

In addition to providing access to information, this publication will enable professionals and visitors alike to receive an overview of both the Scottish stone scene and the richness of materials therein. Much can be gleaned from the principal stone resources described, their relation to the geological framework, and the influence of geomaterials on both the built environment and vernacular styles.

Recording stone resources and comparative properties enables the rational regulation of supplies and the evaluation of geotechnical compliance. Provenance of stone types for matching and replacing is of particular importance to the restoration of heritage sites. The large volume of ongoing research in Scotland on the environmental behaviour of stone is a harbinger of expected future geotechnical contributions.

These items are in line with core activities of IAEG C-10 related to the geotechnical potentials of 'nature's own building material', to which the publication of Stone in Scotland is an important contribution. Thanks are due first and foremost to Ingval Maxwell, OBE, Director TCRE, Historic Scotland, for sponsoring and coordinating the publication; to UNESCO Publishing; the UNESCO Global Earth Observation Section for encouragement and assistance; and the authors and reviewers.

Asher Shadmon
Chairman, Commission, IAEG C-10,
'Building Stones and Ornamental Rock'
IAEG, International Association of
Engineering Geology and the Environment

1. Introduction

There is a growing awareness and appreciation of the role that natural stone plays in Scotland's built heritage and culture. The purpose of this publication is to provide a source of information on the different types and sources of building stone used throughout Scotland. At a time when the demand for indigenous building stone is increasing, both in the repair of Scotland's architectural heritage and in new construction, this volume is intended to provide a framework to help stimulate renewed interest in the once-significant Scottish stone industry and to promote future activity in domestic and export markets.

Scotland is often referred to as 'a nation of stone', typified by its castles and rugged mountain and coastal scenery. Geologically it is a complex assemblage of distinct tectonic fragments brought together during major periods of crustal upheaval at various stages in the Earth's history. It is this geological variety – or 'geodiversity' – that is to a large extent responsible for the diversity in Scotland's stone-built heritage in terms of both materials and architectural style. The fundamental geological properties of a particular rock type in an area have determined how the function and shape of that material has been utilized as a building stone. Local distinctiveness is important in Scotland, as is the cultural identity of a nation with a long and conspicuous history. It is impossible to ignore the stone-built heritage in a nation that boasts treasures on the scale of the sandstone city of Edinburgh – once termed the 'grey Athens of the North'; Aberdeen – 'the granite city'; and Glasgow, where Victorian opulence produced one of the finest late nineteenth century cities in the world. In the modern period of political autonomy following the reformation of the Scottish Parliament in 1999, such national cultural treasures are becoming more important.

Scotland was at one time a major producer of building stone, not only for local use but for export throughout the United Kingdom and on an international scale. The stone industry was of considerable economic significance, and several of its products were internationally renowned, in particular its granite, sandstone and flagstone, which were all widely exported. In addition, technological innovation and mechanization in the quarrying, processing and transportation of stone ensured the continued growth and success of the industry. The production of roofing slate was also of economic importance. From its peak in the nineteenth century, the Scottish stone industry declined rapidly in the early part of the twentieth century. The development of man-made

Figure 1. Museum of Scotland, Edinburgh (1998), an example of modern use of stone cladding with variably coloured Clashach sandstone from Moray. BGS © NERC. Photo: A. McMillan.

Stone in Scotland – ISBN 978-92-3-104031-3 – © UNESCO 2006

building materials, improved transport links, increasing competition and a changing global economy meant that by the end of the twentieth century the stone industry had almost completely disappeared. The skills associated with building stone, such as quarrying and stone masonry, have consesquently become much reduced.

Today a small stone industry survives in Scotland, although much more building stone is imported than is produced within the country. Still, as the value of Scotland's stone-built heritage becomes increasingly recognized, and concepts such as 'local distinctiveness' and 'sense of place' become more important, it is apparent that there is a need for more appropriate types of stone to be used both for conservation and for new building. There is a drive among those involved in the repair and maintenance of historic buildings for a greater understanding of the variety of stone types used in historic buildings; greater understanding will ultimately lead to demand for a wider range of more appropriate materials. This drive is partly a result of increasing standards, better diagnostic methods and tighter planning legislation, but also represents a genuine appreciation and desire to understand traditional building practice, and to improve upon previous attempts at repair and conservation. Demonstrating its role for the future as well as in the past, Scottish stone has recently been used in several prestigious new building projects, such as the Museum of Scotland in Edinburgh, and the new Scottish Parliament building, which opened in 2004 (Figure 1).

If a revival of the Scottish stone industry is to occur, then it is crucial to understand the nature and extent of its former stone industry in order to appreciate the wide variety of stone types that the country possesses and how this variety has influenced its built heritage. This publication is intended to inform those interested in building stone of the diverse resources available throughout Scotland and how they have been used. In this way it provides the background information necessary to move forward. With the foundation of the Scottish Stone Liaison Group in 2000, there is now a mechanism for a more coordinated approach to assessing resources and demand.

Figure 2. Brochel Castle, Isle of Raasay, fifteenth century stronghold of the MacLeod chieftains of Raasay, built from local igneous rock with dressings of white Jurassic sandstone. BGS © NERC. Photo: E. Hyslop.

This volume documents the major stone types used in Scotland and outlines the quarries considered to be of national or regional importance, or to have contributed significantly to local character (Figure 2). It is intended to be an introduction to Scotland's stone resources, compiled principally from data held by the British Geological Survey, including information on currently active quarries (Cameron et al., 2005). This volume looks at the variety of stone types and distribution of former quarries present throughout the country. It should be noted that stone has long been imported into Scotland, for example, sandstone from northern England, Welsh slate and decorative stone from overseas. These sources are not documented in this book.

The publication layout follows the format of previous UNESCO stone publications, using the same major chapter headings. It should be emphasized, however, that the situation in Scotland is different from that of many other stone-producing countries. Once a significant producer and exporter of stone, Scotland is now a country with a relatively small stone industry. Despite this, the geological resources of the country remain large and varied, and it is anticipated that the information presented in this book will provide a framework to stimulate a resurgence of the industry in Scotland.

2. Definitions and terminology

In this volume the term 'building stone' refers to any natural rock used for external or interior parts of buildings, including foundations, roofing slate, paving, kerbstones or for other architectural or structural purposes. The term includes ornamental and monumental stone for decorative and sculptural uses. It does not include crushed stone, aggregate, mortar, concrete or roadstone production. The principal stone types in this book are divided into the following seven categories: sandstone, flagstone, limestone and marble, igneous, granite, metamorphic, and slate. Although these groupings are not strict in the geological sense (for example, slate is a metamorphic rock), they are intended to represent divisions related to the use of building stone. The categories are listed in the definitions of stone types, where their lithological characteristics are defined. Further details are given under the individual headings for different stone types in Chapter Five.

In terms of nomenclature, the approach taken in this volume is to identify stone by its quarry of origin, although commercial names are given where known. The practice of using brand names was not as widely practised in Scotland as in other countries, Scottish stone typically being named after the quarry from which it was extracted. A few notable exceptions exist, such as 'Craigleith sandstone', which was applied to a number of quarries operating in and around Edinburgh, and other generic terms such as 'Aberdeen granite', 'Arbroath pavement' and 'West Highland slate', all referring to products from a number of quarries within a region. In general, the use of a commercial name for a specific building stone product should be discouraged, as it can lead to confusion should that particular stone type be no longer available (for example, if the quarry has become exhausted). In such situations it is not uncommon for a stone from a different quarry to be marketed under the same brand name, despite the fact that the characteristics of stone types from different quarries may be significantly different, even if superficially they appear similar (Shadmon, 2005).

Definitions of stone types used in this volume.

Sandstone

Sandstone is a sedimentary rock consisting of visible mineral grain constituents held together by a natural cement matrix. Sandstones vary widely in terms of constituent minerals, cement types and textures (e.g. grain size, porosity, bed height, etc.), with a wide variety of colours and different performances and applications. They may have sedimentary structures, such as bedding lamination, or contain fossils. Depending upon these factors they respond differently to dressing.

Flagstone

Flagstone (or paving stone) is generally a layered (thinly bedded or laminated) sedimentary rock (typically sandstone or siltstone) capable of being naturally split or riven into large thin slabs. For this purpose it requires characteristics of strength, durability and slip resistance. Flagstone is included as a separate category in this volume because of the significance (past and present) of the flagstone industry in Scotland. Some flagstone quarries are capable of producing stone slates for roofing, while some sandstone quarries have produced flagstone from the more thinly bedded material.

Limestone and Marble

Limestone is a sedimentary rock principally composed of calcium and/or magnesium carbonate, commonly formed from the accumulation of fragments of marine organisms. It is widely variable in colour and texture and may contain fossils on a microscopic or macroscopic scale. Marble is a limestone that has been recrystallized by metamorphism under conditions of heat and pressure. The presence of different metamorphic minerals in marbles can result in widely different appearance, such as the green serpentinite marbles formed by the iron and magnesium rich minerals olivine and serpentine.

Figure 3. Corrennie granite quarry, Aberdeenshire BGS© NERC. Photo: E. Hyslop.

Igneous (excluding granite)

The term is used here for any igneous rock other than granite, ranging from fine to coarse-grained rocks, which are generally hard and crystalline. Basic or intermediate igneous rocks such as basalt, dolerite or gabbro are generally dark in colour and contain little or no quartz. Pale or strongly coloured varieties such as felsite and porphyry are generally associated with volcanic areas. In general, the term 'whinstone' has commonly been used to describe all igneous rocks other than granite: it has sometimes been applied to any dark hard rock, such as the sedimentary greywackes of southern Scotland.

Granite

Granite is a coarse- to medium-grained crystalline igneous rock composed of visible quartz, feldspar and mica, intergrown to give a uniform hard building stone. Granites can vary widely in colour, with common grey and pale red-orange varieties. Granite is included as a separate category from other igneous rocks in this volume because of the former importance of the granite industry in Scotland (Figure 3).

Metamorphic (excluding marble and slate)

Metamorphic rocks are products of the alteration of sedimentary and igneous rocks by temperature and pressure in the Earth's crust. Metamorphism is referred to in relation to 'metamorphic grade', such that a low grade metamorphic rock (e.g. schist) is one which has undergone only a moderate degree of alteration where original features, such as sedimentary bedding, are still preserved. On the other hand, high-grade metamorphic rocks may undergo complete recrystallization or even melting, with destruction of original textures, producing a hard crystalline rock containing distinct metamorphic banding, as does gneiss.

Slate

Slate is a general term used for any stone capable of being uniformly split to form a natural roofing tile. 'True slate' is the product of metamorphic alteration of very fine grained rocks, such as mudstones, resulting in complete recrystallization of the constituent minerals to form a series of parallel cleavage planes along which the stone will readily split into thin sheets. 'Stone slates' are sedimentary rocks (or metamorphic rocks, such as some schists) that do not possess true slaty cleavage, but split into thin slabs along bedding or other planes. Note that slate can also be used as building stone and for paving.

Stone in Scotland – ISBN 978-92-3-104031-3 – © UNESCO 2006

3. Requirements for the selection of stone

The decision to select a particular stone type is dependant upon the ability of that stone to fulfil a number of criteria. Major factors are the functional suitability of the material in terms of its physical characteristics, such as strength, durability, uniformity of texture or colour, and dimensional aspects, such as block size and bed height (for sedimentary rocks). The stone must also be capable of being worked, sawn, dressed and tooled in the required manner. Specific functional requirements demand particular criteria, such as that for slip resistance for natural stone paving, or particular structural characteristics required for use as stone cladding panels. Many of the requisite criteria relating to laboratory testing are given in the appropriate British and European Standard documents relating to a particular product. Testing methods are being harmonized under the European Committee for Standardization (CEN). Although laboratory tests are an important guide to the predicted performance of a stone type, valuable lessons can be learned from the past performance of a stone type in place in a structure which may have been exposed to weathering by the environment for long periods of time.

Issues such as colour and texture are of great importance in the selection of building stone. Natural stone has to look good as well as perform its physical or structural function. The aesthetics of natural stone have always been an important factor, but today it is one of the main reasons why stone is preferred to synthetic building materials in new building projects. For purposes of conservation and repair of historic stone buildings, colour and texture are equally important if a 'like-for-like' repair philosophy is to be adopted

Figure 4. Elgin Cathedral Chapter House (thirteenth century)
© Ingval Maxwell.

for the selection of replacement stone (Figure 4). It should be noted that the natural weathering of stone can also add to its aesthetic characteristics.

One of the most significant issues relating to building stone in Scotland or elsewhere is the sourcing of appropriate material for repairs. Since the vast majority of building stone quarries in Scotland are no longer in operation, it is rarely possible to obtain a particular historic stone type without reopening the original quarry. This has proved possible in only a limited number of cases –mainly for prestigious buildings; the majority of stone used for the repair of Scotland's historic buildings is imported. While this may be satisfactory if the alternative replacement stone has identical characteristics to the original stone, recent studies have shown that the methods used for selection of alternative replacement stone have not always resulted in the most appropriate stone being used for repairs (Hyslop, 2004). Reliance upon criteria such as physical laboratory test data is not sufficient to identify matching stone types where subtle differences in mineral composition, microscopic texture and porosity characteristics might exist. The consequences of using inappropriate replacement stone could be serious, both in terms of changing the appearance of the built heritage and of causing accelerated damage to the original historic fabric. Increased availability of indigenous stone will alleviate this problem as well as increase the choices available for new building projects.

4. History of masonry construction

4.1 Prehistoric structures

The introduction of farming into Scotland during the Neolithic period created a demand for permanent structures from about 4000 BC. The stone building at Knap of Howar, Papa Westray, Orkney, is one of the oldest surviving houses in northwestern Europe, dating from 3500 to 3100 BC (Figure 5). Using local material gathered from the immediate vicinity, the rubble dry-stone construction illustrates that the builders had a remarkable understanding of the structural use of stone and an ability to exploit its natural properties. The best preserved sequence of building developments of the Neolithic period is found at Skara Brae, Orkney (c. 3100–2200 BC). Using similar constructional techniques, the juxtaposition of curvilinear low stone-walled houses and interconnecting passageways created an integrated village community.

The Devonian Old Red Sandstone rocks of Caithness and the Orkney Islands are an ideal material upon which highly developed masonry construction could be effected. This is well illustrated in the Neolithic Maes Howe chambered tomb, dating from c. 2700 BC, where large parallel-sided slabs were used to create a central roofed chamber 4.6 metres square and 3.8 metres high by slightly corbelling out each successive overlying course of stonework.

The double-walled, dry-stone Mousa Broch in Shetland (c. 200 BC–AD 100) represents the ultimate in rubble-stone building construction. Standing 13 metres high, with a 5 metre internal diameter, the tower is the best preserved example of Iron Age architecture in Scotland. Utilizing roughly dressed stone, the concentric walls were built in tightly placed horizontal courses. Larger stones were carefully chosen to serve as stair treads and passageway lintels. Brochs are found throughout Scotland, extending north from the Central Belt.

Continuing the pattern of building in rubble masonry, the multi-period site at Jarlshof, Shetland, was used from 2000 BC to the seventeenth century AD. The earliest buildings on the site consist of small oval-shaped houses, followed by a Bronze Age smithy, and an Iron Age broch and village of round houses. These were overlaid with four wheelhouses dating from the first millennium AD, a Norse settlement, a medieval farm, a sixteenth century Laird's house and, finally, a twentieth century visitors office – all constructed in stone. Spanning this range of dates, the site provides a unique snapshot of how the use of horizontally coursed, dry stone rubble construction continued across the ages.

Figure 5. Knap of Howar, Papa Westray, Orkney (3800 BC)
© Ingval Maxwell.

Figure 6. Suenos Stone, Forres (9th century) © Ingval Maxwell.

4.2 The Romans

Between the first and third centuries AD, the Romans occupied Scotland on three separate occasions. Among their many significant introductions was the use of ashlar masonry: square-dressed stones of uniform course-height, coupled with lime mortar and plastering techniques. This new method of building used locally sourced material, leading to the introduction of quarrying and hewing, lime burning, slaking and mixing techniques, in an integrated process that was to continue until the early twentieth century.

4.3 Ecclesiastical influences

Following the introduction of Christianity to Iona by Saint Columba in AD 563, simple masonry-built churches started to emerge on the peripheral west coast islands and southwest mainland from the eighth century onwards. As the influence took hold, more elaborate structures were built.

During this period, the imagery carved onto the face of free-standing stones of the sixth to ninth centuries exhibited a scholarly competence in the artistic use of the material. While easier-to-work sandstones were preferred, intricately proficient pagan and Christian symbols were also carved into monoliths of granite, schist and other stone types (Figure 6).

Perpetuating the Roman influence, ashlar masonry of the emerging Romanesque period was characteristically 'blocky' in appearance. Quarry material was generally sourced locally for the construction of the numerous medieval cathedrals, abbeys and churches. At Arbroath the stone supply route can still be followed on the nearby foreshore, where grooved parallel runs of cart tracks worn into the bedrock are exposed. These lead to the broken, angular remains of the thinly bedded outcrops from which the abbey building stones were obtained.

4.4 Secular buildings and castles

Characterized by a lightness and airiness, medieval ecclesiastical architecture was built of high quality, dressed and moulded work, in which stone was pushed to its structural limits. On the other hand, secular building had to answer to a completely different set of functional requirements stemming from the need for solid, massive and impenetrable walls. The earliest masonry constructions emerged during the late twelfth century and set the trend for future castle-building. Constructed of coursed rubble-stone, set with pinnings in lime mortar, walls of considerable height, thickness and strength were often erected on naturally defensive sites. Because building economy prevailed, the technique relied much on the compressive strength of the stone for stability. The constructional pedigree of Scottish castle-building is thus firmly linked with prehistoric dry-stone and Roman lime-mortar building technologies.

By the mid-fifteenth century architectural styles began changing. Influenced by Italian developments, the emergence of new ways of thinking and new aesthetic priorities, Scotland's stone architecture became increasingly more domestic, decorative and sophisticated. A new classicism emerged and defensive constructions were systematically replaced by a substantial phase of 'palace' building. This increasingly demanded more refined manifestations in the masonry work; Renaissance detailing became more commonplace. Ashlar masonry was presented on the principle facades, with rubble work relegated to providing the rear elevations, to backing for the dressed work and to the construction of internal walls.

4.5 Urban and rural developments

Although the established urban centres of early eighteenth century Scotland were still medieval in function and layout, from the late 1600s an increasing number of rubble masonry buildings started to emerge using locally quarried supplies of stone. Linking human activity and environmental ideals, the eighteenth century Enlightenment also impacted on this trend (Figure 7). The development of Edinburgh's spacious New Town starting in 1767 translated the building of large country palaces into the design and detailing of entire street façades. The Edinburgh model would influence the rest of the country, with many smaller towns copying the approach, using locally available

Figure 7. Paxton House, Berwick (1758) © Ingval Maxwell.

stone supplies. As the city grew, demand for stone soon outstripped the local availability.

In rural areas during the eighteenth century, clearing the land of glacially deposited stones not only created more workable fields for agricultural needs, but provided stone for field drains, boundary dykes, and the construction of the earliest 'improved' farm buildings. With a view to profits, landowners often opened up new stone quarries and built lime kilns on their estates.

During Victorian times demand for multi-functional farm buildings ran hand in hand with large building programmes in cities and towns. Different domestic needs were satisfied by the construction of stone-built terraced rows, tenements, individual town houses and villas.

As the demand for building stone increased, quarrying activity and masonry skills flourished. Suppliers for Edinburgh, Glasgow and the other Scottish cities were increasingly sourcing stone from further afield. Initially stone came from the Scottish canal network, then, as the railways developed in the mid-nineteenth century, supplies were brought into the Central Belt from all over Scotland. By 1850 it is estimated that some 1,200 commercial building stone quarries were in operation. During the second half of the nineteenth century, production of indigenous sandstone, granite, slate and flagstone was at an all-time high.

The industry benefited enormously from technological innovation, including improvements in the quarrying, processing and transportation of stone. The invention of steam-powered planing, cutting and sawing machinery by the operators of the Angus flagstone quarries led to the massive expansion of the industry during the nineteenth century. In Aberdeenshire the processing of granite was transformed by the introduction of steam-powered polishing machines in the 1830s and the development of the 'Jenny Lind' polishing machine in the 1880s. Steam-powered, compressed-air drilling used in the 1870s was superseded by the first electric-powered drilling in the 1890s. Transportation of stone became increasingly mechanized throughout the nineteenth century. The 'Blondin' overhead cable system used to lift stone within quarries was invented by John Fyfe and first

Figure 8. Geological map of Scotland.

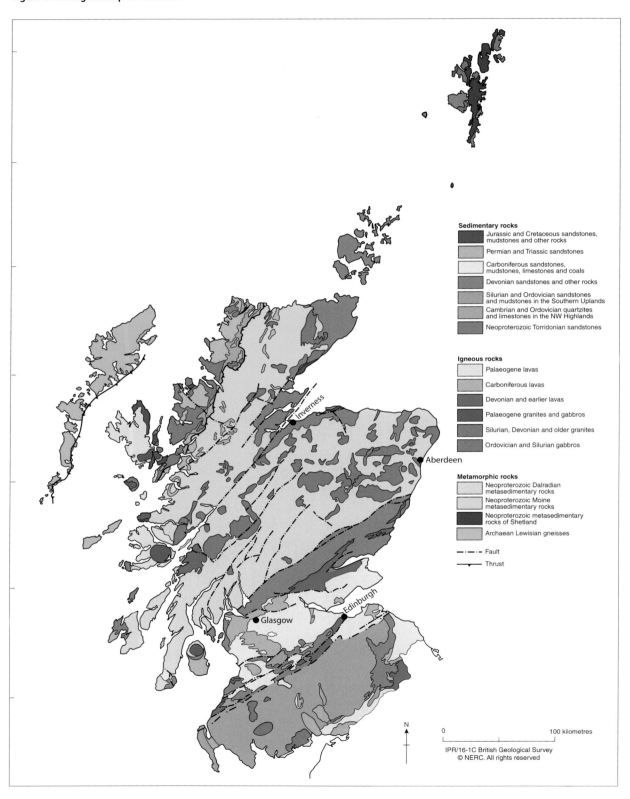

Sedimentary rocks

Jurassic and Cretaceous sandstones, mudstones and other rocks

Permian and Triassic sandstones

Carboniferous sandstones, mudstones, limestones and coals

Devonian sandstones and other rocks

Silurian and Ordovician sandstones and mudstones in the Southern Uplands

Cambrian and Ordovician quartzites and limestones in the NW Highlands

Neoproterozoic Torridonian sandstones

Igneous rocks

Palaeogene lavas

Carboniferous lavas

Devonian and earlier lavas

Palaeogene granites and gabbros

Silurian, Devonian and older granites

Ordovician and Silurian gabbros

Metamorphic rocks

Neoproterozoic Dalradian metasedimentary rocks

Neoproterozoic Moine metasedimentary rocks

Neoproterozoic metasedimentary rocks of Shetland

Archaean Lewisian gneisses

—·—·— Fault

—▼— Thrust

Inverness

Aberdeen

Glasgow

Edinburgh

N

0   100 kilometres

IPR/16-1C British Geological Survey
© NERC. All rights reserved

used in his Kemnay granite quarry in Aberdeenshire in 1873. In most of the main stone producing areas of the nineteenth century quarries became linked by railways, initially to coastal ports and eventually to the national railway networks.

As the rail network continued to grow, new markets opened. Supplies were delivered from as far south as the English Midlands and Wales. Ship-borne trade also flourished. The movement of stone was a two-way process: flagstone was shipped to Europe, the Americas and Asia; Galloway granite found its way to Liverpool's docks and London's embankment; and red sandstone from Dumfriesshire was transported to the eastern seaboard of America and Canada. As the British Empire grew, decorative and exotic stones used for finishing work were also brought in through the Clyde ports. Scotland not only exported stone materials, but also stone technology and masonry skills.

4.6 Twentieth century

Following the Victorian Age, the significant consequences of the depression of the 1920s and of the

two World Wars, a decline in the use of stone occurred during most of the twentieth century. This coincided with the growth of new manufactured materials. Stone made a limited reappearance during the 1930s and mid-1960s, but by this time the market had been transformed into a 'dimensional' stone industry, which meant for practitioners high-class cladding held onto buildings with hidden fixing devices.

The proposed demolition of Edinburgh's eighteenth century George Square during the 1960s was a wake-up call to the amount of traditional stone building that had been lost to the nation. A growing number of people became aware of the value and quality of Scotland's remaining masonry inheritance. By the end of the twentieth century this awareness had increased. People began to realize to what extent the intuitive understanding of how to identify, work and build with stone had been forgotten. Consequently, during the late 1990s much had to be relearned: where to obtain stone, how it should be worked and how it performed in use. Fortunately, a significant number of new initiatives emerged and have continued to progress which aim to put indigenous stone back on top of the building industry agenda.

Figure 9. Diagrammatic chronological table of masonry construction in Scotland.

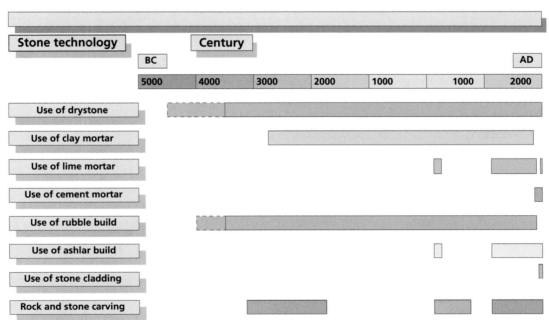

5. Stone resources and distribution

5.1 Geological framework

Scotland is a country with a complex and diverse geology, composed of a large number of distinct components of varying geological age and rock type (Figure 8, Table 1). In the simplest terms, Scotland can be divided into three provinces from north to south: the Highlands and Islands; the Midland Valley; and the Borders and Southern Uplands. The Highlands and Islands are a large area forming the northern part of the country north of the Highland Boundary Fault, and are composed mainly of metamorphic and igneous rocks. The Midland Valley (also known as the Central Belt) is a low-lying belt of mainly sedimentary rocks and igneous lavas, geologically bounded to the north by the Highland Boundary Fault and to the south by the Southern Upland Fault. The Borders and Southern Uplands form the southern part of Scotland, south of the Southern Upland Fault to the border with England, and are composed mainly of low grade metamorphic rocks and notable sandstone and granite.

The Highlands and Islands

The Scottish Highlands is an area of considerable geological complexity. It is dominated by vast areas of ancient metamorphic rock of Precambrian age, by the Dalradian rocks of the Grampian Highlands and the Moine and Lewisian rocks of the Northern Highlands, which are separated by the Great Glen fault. These largely mountainous areas are composed of crystalline, metasedimentary rocks ranging from metasandstones, quartzite, schists, gneiss and less common marble. The degree of metamorphism varies from low-grade metasandstones in the south and east to

very high-grade crystalline rocks such as granite gneiss in parts of the Northern and Grampian Highlands. The northwestern fringes of Scotland contain the Lewisian rocks (which at almost 3,000 million years old are the oldest rocks in the UK), interspersed with the Precambrian Torridonian sedimentary rocks, which are hard semi-crystalline purple-coloured metasandstones. Many of the rock types in the Highlands and Islands are difficult to work using traditional methods and have been used only locally for building purposes. Several major bands of metamorphic mudstones within the Dalradian rocks of the Grampian Highlands have produced major slate belts, which have been quarried on a significant scale.

Igneous rocks are widespread in the Highlands and Islands province, with major granite intrusions of largely Devonian and Carboniferous age occurring throughout the Grampian Highlands and Aberdeenshire, and older Precambrian intrusions in the Northern Highlands. A group of geologically younger (Tertiary or Neogene) intrusions occurs in the western coastal areas and Inner Hebrides, forming large granite and related igneous areas, such as the islands of Skye, Mull and Arran, among others. Several of these granite bodies, particularly in coastal locations, were extensively quarried and exported to many parts of the UK and beyond.

In addition to metamorphic and igneous rocks, large tracts of Devonian sedimentary rocks are present along the northeastern fringes of the Highlands and Islands area, and form the northern isles of Orkney. These mostly red sandstones were deposited in a vast lacustrine environment, producing both flaggy and thickly bedded sandstones, which have long been

Figure 10. Charlotte Square, Edinburgh (1791), part of the Edinburgh New Town, constructed using local high quality Carboniferous sandstone. BGS © NERC Photo: E. Hyslop.

exploited for building stone. Other small pockets of younger Mesozoic sandstones occurring in coastal areas have also been used locally as building stone, such as the Moray Firth area in the east and on the islands of Arran and Mull on the west coast.

Midland Valley

The Midland Valley of Scotland is a fault-bounded lowland area containing mainly sedimentary rocks of Devonian and Carboniferous age, which were deposited in a series of former river systems and desert plains in tropical and arid environments. Most of Scotland's population lives in this area, and these rocks have been extensively exploited as building stones for the construction of the country's major towns and cities (Figure 10). Many of the sandstones are relatively easily worked and were quarried to produce high quality building stones, which were also exported to other parts of Scotland and the UK. A large area of Devonian rocks in the northeast part of the Midland Valley has

been exploited for building stone and flagstone, particularly in the Dundee, Perth and Angus areas.

Igneous rocks are present sporadically across the Midland Valley as intrusive bodies and volcanic deposits of Carboniferous and Devonian age (e.g. East Lothian), but these are difficult to work and generally used only locally for rubble building. Relatively small areas containing red sandstones of Permian and Triassic age are present in the western part of the Midland Valley (e.g. Mauchline in Ayrshire), which because of their thickly bedded nature ('freestones') and relative workability have been quarried as building stone.

Borders and Southern Uplands

The Southern Uplands (including the Borders area) are dominated by large areas of sedimentary 'greywacke' sandstone, siltstone and mudrocks, and basic igneous rocks. The sedimentary rocks are largely Ordovician and Silurian in age and have undergone deformation and low-grade metamorphism to form fissile mudstones and greywacke (sometimes erroneously termed 'whinstone'). These rocks are difficult to work and have generally been used only locally as building stone for rubble walling, although in some areas they have provided reasonable stone slates for roofing. Within the Southern Uplands large inliers of red sandstone have been exploited as building stone, in particular the 'New Red Sandstone' of Permian and Triassic age in Dumfries and Galloway, and the Devonian and early Carboniferous 'Old Red Sandstone' of the eastern Borders area.

Igneous rocks are also present, in particular the large granite masses of the southwest (the so-called Galloway granites), which have been used for building and monumental purposes in Scotland and elsewhere (e.g. Liverpool Docks). Smaller bodies of Devonian and Carboniferous intrusive and volcanic rocks are locally present, particularly in the north and east of the Southern Uplands area, and are mainly used for local construction and contribute significantly to local character.

5.2 Building stone quarries

The following section provides a summary of building stone resources throughout Scotland, compiled from the databases of the British Geological Survey and other available published sources. Individual quarry locations are shown on the accompanying maps (Figures 36-42), each showing a different stone type. It should be noted that the vast majority of quarries are no longer in operation; those that are currently active or are known to have been active in the last decade are indicated. For most of these quarries further information (including samples) may be held in the archives of the British Geological Survey. Because of limitations of scale, not every building stone quarry in the BGS database is included.

It has not been possible to undertake a systematic survey of or visits to the quarries during the production of this volume, and it is therefore not known if the quarries identified contain useable reserves of stone or are capable of further production. The mention of a particular quarry or stone should not be taken as an endorsement of a particular product.

The following section is divided into a number of sub-sections, based on the functional use of stone and the nature of the former industry in Scotland. These sub-sections are: Sandstone; Flagstone; Limestone and marble; Igneous (excluding granite); Granite; Metamorphic; and Slate. Flagstone, granite and slate are described separately from their true geological groupings (sedimentary, igneous and metamorphic rocks, respectively) because of their importance to the Scottish stone industry.

Sandstone

Sandstones of varying geological age and character occur throughout Scotland, and have in many areas been exploited as a building stone (Figures 13-20). Thickly bedded uniform sandstones were prized for producing valuable freestone, and where these occur quarries of significant size were often developed. More thinly bedded sandstone (or flagstone) was exploited for paving or specialist masonry such as copestones, cornices or lintels. In some places, flaggy sandstones were used as stone slates for roofing. A very large number of smaller quarries produced sandstone of smaller block size or poorer quality, which was used locally for rubble building. Quarries traditionally used as much of the resource as possible in order to maximize income, producing high quality freestone from the thickest beds and lesser quality stone for use as rubble from the more thinly bedded parts. Some quarries provided both building sandstone and flagstone for paving or roofing.

Large resources of Carboniferous sandstones occur in the Midland Valley where the bulk of Scotland's population lives and the major urban centres have developed. These resources provided a convenient source of high quality building stone for housing and other developments. The stone is typically quartz-rich and pale in colour, known in Glasgow as 'blonde' sandstone and giving the stone of Edinburgh its characteristic grey colour. Much of this stone was of very high quality in terms of its composition, uniformity and ability to be worked; in the nineteenth century it was

Table 1. Table of stratigraphy, distribution and main uses of the principal types of Scottish building stone (* = active quarries).

Geological Period	Age (million years)	Materials	General distribution	Examples of quarries (past and current)	Main uses
Quaternary (including Neogene)	2	Clay, earth, peat, natural aggregates (sand, gravel) and till	Throughout Scotland		Earth build, and use of clay for inside of stone walls, aggregates for mortars, also brick clay and ochres for colouring lime wash all have an extensive history in Scottish buildings.
Tertiary (Palaeogene)	65	Volcanic and intrusive igneous rocks including granite (e.g. Arran and Skye) and gabbro (e.g. Skye)	Western Highlands & Islands, plus small igneous intrusions throughout Scotland		Locally used, largely for rubble construction and walling (known as whinstone).
Jurassic Cretaceous	200	Sandstone, sometimes calcareous	Isolated coastal areas around northern Scotland e.g. Brora, Mull, Skye.	Carsaig, Clynelish	White sandstone used for dressed stone and ashlar, commonly for local use, though transported to coastal locations around the Scottish Highlands.
Triassic	250	Fluvial red sandstones of Borders; buff siliceous sandstones of Elgin area	Borders (Annan Basin),	Corsehill*, Cove	High quality building sandstone; Corsehill sandstone used throughout the country.
			Elgin (Moray coast)	Spynie*	
Permian	300	Red sandstones	Isolated basins and inliers in SW Scotland, Arran	Locharbriggs*, Corncockle*	Extensive use locally. Widely used in the Central Belt of Scotland following arrival of railway transport and rapid urban expansion during late 19th century; 'freestone' still exported widely.
		Siliceous sandstones of variable colour	Moray Firth	Clashach*	Durable sandstone, exported by sea from late nineteenth century. Used today in Scotland and exported abroad.
Carboniferous	360	Sandstone; basalts and other volcanic rocks	Large areas of the Midland Valley, Solway coast, Berwickshire	Craigleith, Hailes, Binny, Cullalo*, Giffnock, Bishopbriggs, Swinton*	Fluvial siliceous sandstones provided freestone for ashlar masonry and carving, and thinner bedded and laminated stone for cornices, copestones, paving and rubble work. Large number of quarries and the principal building stone used in Central Scotland. Exported from Central Scotland to other parts of Scotland and UK (e.g. London and Belfast), Europe and USA. Now little worked, though large resources. Several sandstone quarries recently reopened. Igneous rock used locally.
Devonian	415	Igneous rocks (andesites and other lavas)	Central Belt	Peppercraig (Haddington), North Berwick Law	Used locally as dressed rubble stone (e.g. East Lothian).
		Caithness Flagstone	Caithness, Orkney and Shetland	Spittal*, Calder*	Major export industry during nineteenth century for flagstone pavement throughout UK and abroad, shipped from coastal ports, later by railway. Also used for roofing. Still worked with large resources.
		Flagstone and sandstone	Angus area, northeastern central Belt	Carmyllie	High quality laminated sandstone used locally as building stone, paving and roofing stone. Large scale industry of flagstones shipped to urban areas throughout UK in late nineteenth and early twentieth centuries. Currently worked only for rubble walling, though large resources.
		Red sandstones (Upper and Lower Old Red Sandstone)	Northern and southern margins of the Central Belt, Borders, parts of Northeast Highlands (Moray Firth, Banffshire), Arran and Kintyre	Kingoodie, Beauly area	Mainly red, brown or purple siliceous fluvial sandstones, commonly conglomeratic, sometimes argillaceous. Supplied building stone to Dundee, Perthshire, Ayrshire, Dunbartonshire, Inverness area, parts of Borders.
		Granite	Aberdeenshire, Dumfries & Galloway	Kemnay*, Rubislaw, Corrennie* Creetown, Dalbeattie*	Extensive local use (e.g. Aberdeen and SW Scotland); widely exported throughout UK. Currently largely quarried for aggregate.
Ordovician Silurian	490	Greywacke, siltstone	Southern Uplands	Stobo (roofing)	Used locally for rubble construction in SW Scotland and Borders. More fissile material worked for roofing 'slate', mainly for local use.
Cambrian	540	Sandstone, quartzite	NW Highlands		Siliceous sandstones, used locally.
		Marble	NW Highlands, Skye	Ledmore*, Torrin*	Variably coloured yellow, green and white marbles (metamorphosed limestone) worked originally for decorative use, currently quarried for aggregate/lime.
Precambrian (including Proterozoic and Archaean)	>540 (oldest Scottish rocks date back to 3 billion years)	Torridonian metasandstone	NW Highlands		Hard, siliceous red and purple recrystallised sandstones, for local use. Supplied local towns and villages in northwest Scotland (e.g. Ullapool).
		Dalradian slate	Argyllshire, Highland Border, Aberdeenshire/Banffshire	Ballachulish, Easdale, Foundland, Aberfoyle	Former extensive industry largely exported by sea to supply urban development in central Scotland during nineteenth century.
		Dalradian and Moine schist and gneiss	Northwest Highlands & Islands, Grampian and Central Highlands		Metamorphic and igneous rocks used for local building.
		Lewisian gneiss & marble	Northwest Highlands & Islands	Iona	Metamorphic and igneous rocks, used locally for building. Marbles historically exported from Iona and Tiree for decorative purposes.

exported by sea from both the west and east coasts to supply areas such as Ireland and northwest Scotland. Some of the Midland Valley sandstones were so valuable that they were worth extracting by underground mining (e.g. Bishopbriggs Quarry, near Glasgow) and exported for the construction of prestigious buildings in London and overseas (e.g. Craigleith Sandstone, from Edinburgh).

The large tract of Devonian sandstones along the northern and eastern fringe of the Midland Valley provides a source of brown and dark red sandstones ('Old Red Sandstone'), which were used extensively in cities such as Dundee, Perth and many surrounding towns and villages, giving buildings in these areas a distinctive appearance. In addition, the thinly bedded nature of some of the strata led to the development of a large flagstone industry, which exported stone to other parts of the UK and overseas. Red sandstones of Permian and Triassic age ('New Red Sandstone'), commonly of eolian (i.e. windblown) origin are found in parts of southwest Scotland, particularly in Ayrshire and Dumfriesshire. These distinctive, brightly coloured freestones give a particular character to these areas, and were made widely available to other parts of the country as the railway network expanded in the late nineteenth century. Such stone is commonly used as dressed stone quoins and surrounds to windows and doors in combination with lesser quality local stone, which was used for the rubble walling. The vivid colour of these red sandstones has not diminished over time.

Other distinctive varieties of sandstone occur around the country, and are important locally. For example, the use of dark red Precambrian Torridonian sandstone of the Northwest Highlands has had a significant impact on local building styles, because its crystalline nature makes it very difficult to work and suitable mostly for rubble work. In parts of southern Scotland, relatively workable sandstone was used in combination with the local greywacke and whinstone rubble.

In Caithness and Orkney, local sandstones of Devonian age provided excellent building stones, and a number of large quarries supplied high quality building stone that was transported around the area by sea. A number of small geological inliers of Jurassic and Cretaceous age occur around the coastal fringes of the Scottish Highlands, such as on the Islands of Skye and Mull, and in the Brora area. White sandstones from these inliers were one of the few sources of workable freestone in the Highlands, and were transported around the coast beginning in medieval times.

Sandstone quarries in the Borders and Southern Uplands

▶ (i) Eastern area

A large outcrop of Old Red Sandstone of Devonian age occurs along a roughly north–south axis from southeast of Hawick to the northeast coast near Dunbar. The stone was quarried in a large number of locations, most significantly around the larger Borders towns of Jedburgh, Melrose, Coldstream, Hawick, Kelso and St Boswells, although numerous smaller quarries also existed.

The stone is typically a reddish colour, though ranges from white, yellow and greenish to pink, with some pale-grey or buff variations. All variations, from freestone to irregular, lenticular and flaggy beds, are present. Some of the more vivid red sandstones contain distinctive white reduction spots.

A number of quarries exported high quality sandstone from the region; for example, the Swinton quarries (including Whitsome Newton quarry) produced pink-tinted and yellowish buff sandstones. Stone was first produced on a significant scale here in 1791, and was transported to Edinburgh in the late nineteenth and early twentieth centuries. Swinton quarry has recently reopened.

▶ (ii) South and Western Area

Large inliers of mostly eolian red sandstones of Permian age, known as the 'New Red Sandstone', occur in southwest Scotland, with four main outcrops in the areas around Dumfries, Lochmaben and Thornhill, and Stranraer to the west. Related deposits occur to the north around Mauchline and across the English border to the south around Penrith. Similar red sandstones of Permian and Triassic age also occur straddling the border with England in the areas around Annan and

Carlisle. These deposits have long been exploited in a series of major quarries throughout the district, for example, at Gatelawbridge, Newton, Corncockle, Corsehill, Locharbriggs, Knowehead and Cove.

Some of these quarries were active as early as the seventeenth century, then saw a rapid expansion during the late nineteenth century with the development of the railway network. Red sandstone was particularly popular for the expanding urban areas in the Scottish Central Belt during the early twentieth century. For example, the Locharbriggs quarry employed 267 men in 1899. Following a period of decline during the twentieth century, several of these quarries have reopened.

Relatively small outcrops of pale Carboniferous sandstone exist in some parts of the Borders and were significant locally, such as the Whita Hill quarry at Langholm.

Sandstone quarries in the Highlands and Islands

▶ (i) Northeast

A large number of sandstone quarries exist in the Northeast Highlands, and are associated with the vast outcrops of Devonian red sandstones stretching from Orkney and Caithness along the coast to the Moray Firth. Large outcrops occur particularly in the Cromarty, Beauly and Moray Firths and Black Isle areas.

The Devonian sandstone (or 'Old Red Sandstone') has been widely used in the coastal areas, where many quarries have exploited stone for local use. The stone was also transported inland for use as dressed stone in combination with rubble of metamorphic and igneous rocks. The Devonian rocks are typically dark red or brown (though some pink, yellow and white varieties exist), and have bed heights ranging from thick bedded freestone to laminated flaggy material. Examples of such quarries, which provided stone for local buildings, occur around the towns of Evanton, Dornoch, Tain, Beauly and Nairn. Typically, many different towns and villages were supplied by their own quarries.

In the Black Isle and along the Nairn coast one of the largest outcrops of Devonian sandstone led to an abundance of small quarries in red sandstone, which supplied stone exclusively for local use. Some 36 individual quarries are recorded in this area alone.

Permian and Triassic sandstones form much smaller outcrops along the east coast, the most notable being on the Morayshire coast and smaller outcrops near Brora. Where present as freestone these sandstones were favoured for their pale colour and siliceous nature. For example, the Clynelish quarry at Brora produced a yellowish-white freestone, which gives a distinctive appearance to buildings in the village. The so-called 'Hopeman Sandstones' have been quarried over a long period, and due to their coastal location were shipped southwards to the main population centres of Scotland. These quarries were quick to employ new technology in the boom years of the late nineteenth century, including their own railway lines. Quarries such as Clashach and Greenbrae at Hopeman, and Cutties Hillock and Spynie near Elgin, were active in the second half of the nineteenth century, producing pale siliceous freestones whose colours range from white and yellow to pink. Following a period of decline in the first half of the twentieth century, some of the quarries reopened towards the end of the century. Today, the Clashach quarry supplies stone across the UK and abroad, and is in much demand for both conservation and new building projects.

▶ (ii) Grampian Highlands

Relatively few sandstone resources suited to building purposes exist in the Grampian Highlands. Outcrops of Devonian red sandstone in Banffshire and Turriff provided high quality stone, which was used for dressed stonework in combination with igneous and metamorphic rubble. A number of sandstone quarries exploited the Devonian Rhynie outlier in Aberdeenshire, and provided red and white freestone used extensively throughout the district for dressed work, such as at Kildrummy, Rhynie and Monquhitter. Some of this stone was transported to Aberdeen for use as quoins, lintels and other dressings, in combination with local granite.

▶ (iii) Western Highlands and Argyll

Sandstone suitable for building purposes is not common in the Western Highlands, although a number of specific outcrops have long been exploited,

28

particularly where coastal locations allowed transportation. Typically such stone has been used for prestigious ornamental or sculptural work, or as dressed stone in combination with metamorphic and igneous rubble.

In southernmost Argyll, Devonian red sandstones are present; typically coarse grained or conglomeratic, they have long been exploited for local use (e.g. in Cowal). Jurassic sandstone is present in relatively restricted outcrops and has long been prized as a freestone which is relatively easily worked. For example, the pale greenish or buff Jurassic sandstone from Carsaig quarry on the Ross of Mull was widely used from medieval times, and was relatively easily exported due to its coastal setting. On the Isle of Raasay a large quarry in fallen blocks of white to greenish-grey calcareous sandstone was locally used in the early nineteenth century, being transported by sea.

(iv) Northern Isles

The Devonian sandstones of Orkney have provided stone for building from earliest times. A number of quarries provided freestone, such as at Clestrain where fine grained grey siliceous sandstone was taken for use in Kirkwall and Stromness. Several large freestone quarries operated on the island of Eday, producing a distinctive yellow freestone suitable for decorative work. Devonian Middle Old Red Sandstone was exploited in a number of quarries on Shetland.

Sandstone quarries in Central Scotland

(i) Western Central Belt (including Glasgow)

Records show that over sixty large-scale commercial sandstone quarries operated in the western part of Central Scotland. Many of these supplied stone to satisfy demand from urban development in Glasgow and surrounding areas such as Ayrshire and Lanarkshire. Large areas of pale (or 'blonde') Carboniferous sandstone are present, as well as dark red Devonian sandstones.

The city of Glasgow was originally supplied by numerous quarries of Carboniferous sandstone, which would now lie within the city limits, but have long disappeared. Quarries in different parts of the city produced stone giving a distinctive appearance to differ-

ent areas. For example, a coarse, brownish sandstone containing plant remains was used in the Govan area, while reddish sandstone with clay clasts was used in the Cambuslang district.

Quarries in the Giffnock and Bishopbriggs areas of Glasgow were particularly extensive, producing large blocks of high quality pale-coloured freestone known as 'Liver rock'. This was used for high quality work through the city, and also exported to Belfast, America and South Africa. The stone was of sufficient quality that underground mining took place at both locations. These quarries were most active in the late nineteenth century coinciding with the large expansion of urban Glasgow.

In the southern part of the region, local quarries supplied smaller towns with particular sandstone, such as the red Devonian sandstone used in Ardrossan, Kilmarnock and Largs, and the pale sandstones from Troon and Ayr.

(ii) East Central Belt (Lothians and Edinburgh)

Records exist for over seventy sandstone quarries throughout the Lothians. In the Edinburgh area a large number of major sandstone quarries exploited mostly Carboniferous sandstone (Figures 11 and 36). These developed in order to supply the vast urban expansion from the late eighteenth to the early twentieth century. A number of the major quarries are now contained within the city limits, and many of these sites have been infilled and developed. Over time, as transport systems improved, stone was supplied from quarries throughout the Lothians, and subsequently imported from farther away. Today there are no active sandstone quarries in the area.

The best known Edinburgh quarry was Craigleith, which produced a fine grained, pale grey, quartz-rich sandstone, used extensively in the city and also exported throughout the UK (notably to London) and overseas. It was worked from the early seventeenth century to the mid-twentieth century, when it was infilled. Other former quarry sites within the city which provided significant quantities of stone have not been redeveloped (e.g. Craigmillar, Hailes, Ravelston, Barnton Park, and others). A greater number of smaller quarries existed, which now also lie within the city boundaries and have been infilled and redeveloped. The earliest records show production as far back as the fourteenth century (e.g. Craigmillar quarry), while some were active as late as the 1940s (e.g. Hailes and Hawkhill Wood quarries). Issues regarding obtaining supplies of appropriate sandstone for the repair and maintenance of Edinburgh's built heritage are discussed further in Annex II.

West Lothian contains approximately eighteen significant quarries of Carboniferous sandstone, such as Hermand, Hopetoun, Humbie, Binny and Dalmeny. Many of these supplied Edinburgh during the nineteenth and early twentieth centuries, using the emerging canal system and railway network. Some of these quarries brought distinctive stone to Edinburgh, such as the thinly bedded, laminated Hermand stone and the fine grained, pale brown Binny, much favoured for prestigious buildings in Edinburgh. Many of the quarries had ceased production by 1914, and although no sandstone quarries are currently active in West Lothian, some sites are still undeveloped and may be capable of reopening. Binny quarry was reopened in 1997 on a temporary basis to supply stone for repairs to the Scott Monument in Edinburgh.

Other quarries in West Lothian made significant contributions to the local stone-built heritage. Quarries such as those supplying Linlithgow (e.g. Hillhouse, Cauldhame and Kingscavil) provided a distinctive reddish brown sandstone with a laminated texture. Craigton quarry near Philipstoun had a chocolate-brown colour, and was used in both Edinburgh and Glasgow, operating until the 1930s.

Approximately fifteen significant sandstone quarries are recorded in East Lothian, which mainly provided stone for local needs. Sandstone was obtained from both Devonian and Carboniferous outcrops in the area, with both white and red colours. Most of the Devonian quarries produced a deep red stone, such as that from several quarries around Dunbar, giving the town its distinctive character. Devonian Upper Old Red Sandstone typically has a lighter red colour with white spots, such as that used in the village of Garvald. A number of quarries operated in Carboniferous sandstone near Tranent until the first few decades of the twentieth century, producing yellowish white, pale brown and grey stone.

A number of quarries in Midlothian exploited yellowish-brown Carboniferous sandstones for mainly local use, for example, around the towns of Penicuik, Newtongrange and Gorebridge (Figure 12). Some of these quarries continued into the early twentieth century. Several quarries provided stone for transportation south into Peeblesshire for use as stone dressings with local whinstone and greywacke rubble (e.g. in Carlops).

▶ (iii) Northeast Central Belt

Extensive outcrops of sandstone occur throughout the northeast part of the Central Belt. Devonian sandstones, which are generally red or brown coloured and argillaceous (i.e. mud- or clay-bearing) are most common in Angus, Dundee and Perthshire. Pale quartz-rich sandstones (commonly containing mica, and carbonaceous matter) are more prevalent in Fife, Kincardineshire, Stirlingshire and Clackmannanshire. Records exist for over forty commercial-scale sandstone quarries in the region, ranging from small quarries, which were operated largely by hand for local use, to large-scale operations, which supplied stone to cities throughout the UK and overseas.

In Angus and Dundee, quarries in Devonian sandstone typically produced stone ranging in colour from reddish brown to pinkish grey. Most were active in the eighteenth and nineteenth centuries, closing in the early twentieth century, and some were still operating supplying local building needs until the mid-twentieth century. A number of quarries supplied coarse grained, red and pink sandstone to local villages and towns such as Brechin, Edzell and Fettercairn.

Large quarries at Kingoodie and Leoch near Dundee produced fine grained compact stone, which was extensively used in the nineteenth century for polished ashlar in Dundee. Large blocks up to 15 metres in length for monumental and harbour construction were exported by sea from Kingoodie.

In many parts of Perthshire, Devonian reddish brown and grey sandstones were exploited largely for local use (e.g. in Auchterarder, Dunblane and Bridge of Earn).

In Fife, quarries of mostly Carboniferous whitish or grey sandstone were exploited for both local use and for export. Several large quarries near Burntisland (Grange, Newbigging and Cullalo) supplied high quality pale- or creamy-coloured freestone stone throughout the region and to cities such as Dundee, Edinburgh and Glasgow. The quarries were most active during the nineteenth century when, for example, the Grange quarry employed 110 men in 1902. Production had almost ceased by 1914, although some operated intermittently until the mid-twentieth century. Cullalo (Cullaloe) quarry produced a high quality, pale grey-white stone, favoured in Edinburgh. The quarry employed 50 men in 1898, but then declined and worked intermittently until 1948. It was reopened in 2004 largely to supply conservation needs in Edinburgh and locally. The local Duloch and Dunfermline Park (Millhill) quarries supplied medium grained sandstone, used for much of Dunfermline.

In Kincardineshire and Clackmannanshire a number of large quarries produced fine grained, whitish Carboniferous sandstone, such as the Longannet and Sands quarries near Kincardine, exported by sea along the Firth of Forth. Records show these quarries operated from the late eighteenth century into the early twentieth century, supplying high quality ashlar stone to Edinburgh. Longannet quarry employed 155 men in 1910, but major works had ceased by 1910. Smaller quarries supplied material for local use, such as a red Carboniferous Sandstone from Sauchie, much used in Alloa and the neighbourhood.

In Stirlingshire, both Devonian and Carboniferous sandstones were quarried. In general, the Devonian red sandstones were exploited for local use (e.g. in Cauldhame, Kippen and Bridge of Allan), while larger quarries exported high quality white Carboniferous sandstone freestone to the urban centres of the Central Belt. Larger scale quarries to the south and east of Stirling, such as Dunmore (Airth), Plean/Kenmure and Polmaise (Cowie), exploited fine grained, cream coloured freestone used for building in both Glasgow and Edinburgh during the late nineteenth century.

Figure 11. House in the Edinburgh Old Town, constructed from local sandstones and basaltic rock as random rubble. BGS © NERC Photo: A. McMillan.

Figure 12. Local Carboniferous sandstone rubble construction, Penicuik Estate, Midlothian. BGS © NERC Photo: E. Hyslop.

Figure 13. Cullalo quarry, Fife, an important producer of high quality sandstone for local use and in Edinburgh during the nineteenth century, reopened in 2004. BGS © NERC Photo: E. Hyslop.

Figure 14. Edzell Castle garden, constructed in 1604 using local Devonian red sandstone. BGS © NERC Photo: E. Hyslop.

Figure 15. Culzean Castle, Ayrshire (1777–1792) originally constructed from local sandstone, extensively repaired in the twentieth century using paler sandstone from England. BGS © NERC Photo: E. Hyslop.

Figure 16. Town houses constructed from pale sandstones of local origin, Elgin. BGS © NERC Photo: E. Hyslop.

Figure 17. Noltland Castle, Orkney (1560–73), a heavily-fortified castle built for the Sheriff of Orkney. © Ingval Maxwell.

Stone in Scotland – ISBN 978-92-3-104031-3 – © UNESCO 2006

Figure 18. Sweetheart Abbey, Dumfries and Galloway, a late thir-teenth and early fourteenth century Cistercian Abbey built from local Permian red sandstone. BGS © NERC Photo: A. McMillan.

Figure 19. Dunglass Collegiate Church, East Lothian, constructed in the fifteenth and sixteenth centuries from local Carboniferous sandstone. BGS © NERC Photo: A. McMillan.

Figure 20. Corncockle Quarry, Dumfries and Galloway, which supplied Permian red sandstone to urban areas in Central Scotland during the nineteenth century. Reopened 1986. BGS © NERC Photo: A. McMillan.

Flagstone

The production of flagstone has long been an important part of the stone industry in Scotland, and was particularly active in the nineteenth century when flagstone was in great demand for urban development throughout the UK. Significant resources of flagstone are present in several parts of Scotland, principally Caithness and Orkney 'Caithness flagstone' and Angus 'Arbroath pavement' and 'Carmyllie flagstone', where a large number of quarries used local ports for export to the Central Belt, England and overseas. Geologically both areas are dominated by thinly laminated sandstones and siltstone of Devonian age deposited in a shallow lacustrine environment, although the characteristics and appearance of the flagstone vary significantly between the two areas. Both areas also produced 'stone slates' for roofing purposes primarily for local use, and some quarries specialized in producing roofing slates for export, mainly to the Central Belt.

In other parts of Scotland flagstone was produced locally in areas of sandstone production, exploiting thinly bedded sandstones commonly found in existing sandstone quarries. For example, a number of sandstone quarries in the Midland Valley were known to have produced paving stones for Edinburgh.

Caithness and Orkney flagstone

The Devonian flagstone of Caithness and Orkney is typically a distinctive dark grey, fine grained siltstone. Variations in mineral content can produce a paler, more orange-brown coloured stone. It is easily split along bedding planes, which generally have a rough surface texture with good slip resistance quality. These laminated siltstones and sandstones extend over a wide area of Caithness and Orkney and have long been exploited. During the nineteenth century the village of Castletown became the main seaport, exporting vast amounts of flagstone throughout the UK and abroad. Railway transport also became important. Caithness flagstone is recorded as having been used in over a hundred towns and cities throughout the British Isles, and international destinations included Hamburg, India, Australia and South America.

Figure 21. Blocks of Caithness flagstone stacked on the quarry floor for processing as paving slabs and building stone. BGS © NERC Photo: E. Hyslop.

Today the Caithness flagstone industry is enjoying a revival as natural paving is becoming more popular for streetscape schemes, landscaping and indoor use (Figure 21).

Angus pavement quarries

The Devonian sedimentary rocks of the Angus region were exploited for paving stone, known collectively as 'Arbroath pavement' after the coastal town of Arbroath from where it was exported by sea throughout the UK, to mainland Europe, the US and Australia. Some of the larger quarries (or groups of quarries) were individually known, such as 'Carmyllie flagstone', which was used in Edinburgh, Glasgow and London (among other cities) during the nineteenth century. After 1800 the pavement industry began to expand from existing quarries which supplied stone slate for roofing in Angus and Dundee and also shipped stone to Edinburgh and East Lothian. The stone was also used extensively locally for building purposes. A review of the Angus pavement quarries is given by Mackie (1980).

Other Flagstone quarries

A large number of quarries existed throughout Scotland, supplying flagstone mainly for local use.

For example, Devonian sandstones were exploited at Dornoch in Sutherland and West Linton in the Borders. Carboniferous sandstones were used as paving stone for urban development in the Central Belt; for example, stone from Hailes quarry was used in Edinburgh, and paving stone was transported into Edinburgh from West Lothian and Stirlingshire by canal in the early nineteenth century.

Metamorphic rocks were also quarried for flagstones, in particular Dalradian micaceous schist from Aberdeenshire and Banffshire, which were also used locally for building. A number of quarries near Tomintoul produced paving slabs 2 metres in length for local use, and Moine schist from the Ross of Mull was used for the restoration of Iona Abbey. Many of these quarries also provided stone slates for local use.

Limestone and marble

There is little tradition for building with limestone in Scotland, although local examples exist in several areas. For example, large quantities of Precambrian Dalradian limestone were used in the walls of houses in Banffshire (Robertson et al., 1949). In some areas, for example, around Ballachulish, Dalradian limestone outcrops were exploited on a small scale and the stone can be seen in traditional buildings of rubble construction. Limestone was extensively quarried and burnt in kilns for agricultural use as a soil-improving agent and for the production of lime mortar and plaster. The main deposits of limestone occur in the Carboniferous rocks of the Midland Valley, but others are found scattered throughout the Highlands and Southern Uplands, and these were exploited even in the most remote areas.

Scotland has a number of true marbles (limestone recrystallized by metamorphism) in the metamorphic belts of the Highlands, which have been exploited as a building material, mainly for decorative use. These are typically variable, green-coloured serpentinite marbles with distinctive textures, although so-called pink and blue varieties also occur. Several of the quarries were active intermittently from the eighteenth century, and most ceased production in the early twentieth century. Most of the quarries were in coastal areas and

Figure 22. Torrin marble quarry, Isle of Skye, a pale green serpentine marble formerly worked for decorative use, today largely crushed for aggregate. BGS © NERC Photo: E. Hyslop.

used sea transport to the main urban centres to the south and also into England and Continental Europe. The industry survives in a few parts of the Highlands, although today the material is destined for a different market (e.g. aggregate and concrete production), and is mainly transported by road.

Marbles of Precambrian age from the Lewisian rocks were exploited on the islands of Iona and Tiree. 'Iona Marble' is a distinctive pale green, serpentine marble with white mica, giving the distinctive 'Iona Silverstone'. 'Tiree Marble' is a distinctive, pink mottled marble with greenish patches, which was prized for its unusual appearance. Marbles from the Precambrian Dalradian rocks were quarried at Portsoy in Aberdeenshire, where a dark, serpentine marble was exported by sea to Europe, and at Glen Tilt, Blair Atholl, where a banded micaceous (phlogopite) marble with yellow-green mottles was exploited. An unusual pale blue-grey coloured, granular marble, was quarried in Glen Dessary, near Loch Arkaig. Cambrian-Ordovician marbles have been extensively quarried on the Isle of Skye, where large slabs and blocks of pale greenish-yellow, serpentine 'Skye Marble' were widely exported in the early nineteenth century. By the early twentieth century the industry had declined to supply only small chips for terrazzo mosaic. Today marble is still quarried at Torrin on Skye (Figure 22), along with the vivid, yellow green Cambrian-Ordovician 'Ledmore Marble' from Ledmore in Sutherland, both quarries principally producing aggregate.

While discussing limestone it is important to mention that Scotland has a strong tradition of rendering the exterior of stone buildings with lime mortar – or 'harling' – and a final coating of lime 'wash'. These traditional finishes are responsible for the characteristic appearance of much of the nation's vernacular buildings. The application of lime was primarily functional in origin, providing a protective layer against the harsh Scottish climate, keeping wind and water out of buildings. Where high quality stone was not available or could not be afforded, it also served to cover and protect relatively poor quality rubblework, providing a sacrificial layer preserving the underlying fabric of the building. Lime washes were also decorative, and pigments such as ochre from natural deposits of iron oxides were added to create an attractive appearance. The significance of external lime plasters in defining the character of Scottish traditional buildings should not be underestimated, and in 1994 the Scottish Lime Centre was established to promote the use of traditional lime coatings and mortars. It is beyond the scope of this volume to list the huge numbers of limestone quarries in Scotland, and those described above are those which as far as is known produced limestone for building purposes.

Igneous (excluding granite)

Igneous rocks other than granite occur widely throughout Scotland and have been extensively quarried locally, largely for use as aggregate and roadstone. A large number of quarries are still in production today for this purpose. Fine grained, dark coloured igneous rock, generally referred to as whinstone, is common

in many parts as small intrusions or larger areas of lava flows, such as the Carboniferous volcanic areas in the Midland Valley and Borders, and the Tertiary volcanic areas of the west coast. These rocks have been exploited locally as a rubble stone for building and walling. Despite not being intensively quarried or exported as a building stone, this stone type forms an important and distinctive component of Scotland's built heritage.

The term 'whinstone' is generally poorly defined and commonly incorrectly used to describe any fine grained, dark rock type with unpredictable fractures that make it difficult to work. Geologically, whinstone is a fine grained, dark coloured igneous rock of mafic composition (i.e. quartz-poor). The use of the term to describe sedimentary rocks such as greywacke sandstone is incorrect and leads to confusion.

Other less common but distinctive igneous intrusions, such as porphyry, microgranite and trachyte, have been used as ornamental stone and paving blocks. In general terms these are fine or coarse grained igneous rocks that may be strongly or weakly coloured, but are distinct from granite. Although generally difficult to work, they have been valued because of their attractive appearance and durability.

Dark coloured, igneous rocks, such as basalt, diorite and dolerite, are still quarried in the Central Belt (e.g. at Duntilland and Hillend quarries in Lanarkshire,

Figure 23. Traditional hand production of granite setts for road paving; workmen in their traditional huts or 'scathies', Kemnay granite quarry, Aberdeenshire 1939. BGS © NERC.

Figure 24. Victorian church, Aberdeenshire, constructed from roughly squared local grey granite rubble and red sandstone dressings. BGS © NERC Photo: E. Hyslop.

Figure 25. Traditional roadway using 'horonizing', splits from whinstone sett production, Musselburgh, East Lothian. BGS © NERC Photo: E. Hyslop.

and at Bangley quarry in East Lothian) and at Reay in Caithness. Although principally aggregate quarries, stone is available for building (for both new construction and repair of historic buildings), walling and paving (e.g. kerbstones) (Figure 25). Other quarries that historically supplied similar stone for local building (e.g. in Aberdeenshire) are documented, but no longer in operation. Other types of igneous rocks with more distinct appearance have been used for local building throughout Scotland. For example, volcanic rocks of variable red, purple, yellow and green colours have been used in East Lothian and the Borders (e.g. in Haddington and Melrose), and Campbeltown in Argyll.

Decorative igneous rock has been quarried since the mid-nineteenth century from the island of Ailsa Craig in Ayrshire, where a blueish grey microgranite has been used for curling stones and high quality setts. Porphyritic microgranite was extensively quarried in Argyll for paving stones, principally at Furnace quarry on Loch Fyne, where a distinctive pink or grey stone was shipped to Glasgow for kerbstone and setts. Other distinctive igneous rocks were also exploited, such as the lustrous 'Kentallenite' or 'black granite', valued as a polished stone for monumental work, from Kentallen on Loch Linnhe.

Granite

In this volume granites are considered separately from other igneous rocks because of their importance to the stone industry in Scotland. Scotland has a large number of granite intrusions, ranging in geological age from Precambrian to late Tertiary, with a peak of activity in Silurian, Devonian and Carboniferous times. Many have been exploited locally as a building material, but in several areas they were quarried on a larger scale for export.

The principal areas of granite quarries were Aberdeenshire in the Northeast Highlands, the Mull and Oban areas of the Western Highlands and the Galloway granites of the southwest Southern Uplands (Anderson, 1939). As well as strength and durabililty, Scottish granite was valued for its attractive appearance, with stone from the different regions having different characteristics – for example, the silver grey granites of Galloway, the deep reds from Ross of Mull and Peterhead and the salmon pink of Corrennie in Aberdeenshire. Granite was widely exported during the nineteenth century and valued for its structural qualities as a building stone (favoured for the foundations of major constructions), for roadways and paving (setts or cobbles, and kerbstones) and also polished for decorative and monumental use (Figures 23 and 24).

Almost all the significant quarries were coastal or linked to a coastal port for export by sea. In Aberdeenshire the granite industry was of huge importance to the local economy, and materials and skills were so plentiful that much of the city of Aber-

Figure 27. Duke of Gordon statue (1842), Golden Square, Aberdeen carved from local granite. © Ingval Maxwell.

Figure 26. Marischal College, Aberdeen, completed in 1906, is the largest granite building in the United Kingdom, built using local Kemnay granite. Photo: M. Young.

deen was constructed from granite, despite it being a difficult and expensive stone to work (Diack, 1941) (Figures 26 and 27). A relatively sophisticated transportation system (canal and railways) allowed material from quarries further inland to be transported to the coast, and the stone was exported in great quantities to places such as London, where Aberdeen granite was first used for paving in 1764.

The quarries in the Western Highlands, specifically the Ross of Mull quarry and the Bonawe and Ballachulish quarries near Oban, were directly on the coast, and were favoured for major construction projects, such as lighthouses and roadstone. The Galloway granites known as 'Creetown' or 'Silver-Grey', are a silver-grey speckled granite that was used in cities on the west coast of the UK, in particular for the construction of the Liverpool docks. These quarries employed as many as 400 men in 1900. In addition, local use of granite as a building stone has produced distinctive townscapes, such as Dalbeattie, which was built largely from grey Galloway granite.

The major granite quarries in Aberdeenshire have a long, continuing history of supplying stone for the construction of prestigious buildings throughout the UK and beyond. For example, the silver-grey coloured Kemnay granite was used for such diverse projects as the Forth Railway Bridge near Edinburgh (1885), the Queen Victoria Memorial in London, and as cladding for the new Scottish Parliament in Edinburgh (2004). Several of the quarries are still open today, although they largely produce crushed aggregate. The quarry at Tormore in the Ross of Mull produced the largest granite blocks in the UK at 16 metres in length, and some blocks were exported to the US. It was used in the construction of Westminster Bridge and Blackfriars Bridge in London. Large reserves and block sizes are still available. Quarries that had a more limited block size specialized in producing setts for paving.

Metamorphic rocks

Metamorphic rocks occur principally in the Scottish Highlands and the Southern Uplands, and in both these regions the stone has been used for building purposes. Some metamorphic rocks can be difficult to work, being hard and crystalline as a result of high-grade metamorphism (e.g. the gneiss of the Northwest Highlands) (Figure 28), while others are brittle and fragmentary as a result of low-grade metamorphism (e.g. the greywacke shales of the Southern Uplands). In certain areas metamorphic rocks may possess a schistosity that allows them to be split in a predictable manner, making them more useable as building materials. In several areas metamorphic rock (other than true slate) is fissile enough to have been used locally as roofing stones. Because of the importance of the slate and flagstone industries to Scotland, these topics are discussed in other sections.

As a result of the characteristics described above, most metamorphic rock has been exploited only locally for building purposes. Throughout the Scottish Highlands, suitable schist, gneiss, quartzite and other lithologies have been locally quarried. In particular, chlorite schist has been widely used throughout the Grampian Highlands, as it can be relatively easily worked and splits into thick blocks. Examples of its use for local building can be found in the towns of Inverary, Argyll, and Aberfeldy, Perthshire, and its use in medieval sculptures can be seen throughout Argyll.

In the Southern Uplands, less intractable metamorphosed mudrocks and siltstones have been used for rubble building, often in combination with imported sandstone for the more formal, dressed stone around openings and quoins. This pattern can also be seen throughout the Highlands, where the more decorative parts of buildings, or those requiring carving, commonly use imported sandstone, particularly in coastal areas where more suitable stone was brought in by sea. The use of local materials throughout these areas of Scotland has led to a strong local distinctiveness in building stone and architectural style (Figure 29,30 and 31).

Figure 28. Traditional farm building constructed from field boulders of Precambrian Torridonian metasandstone and Lewisian gneiss, Northwest Highlands. BGS © NERC Photo: E. Hyslop.

Figure 29. Metamorphosed Silurian mudstone rubble with sandstone dressings, Peebles. BGS © NERC Photo: E. Hyslop.

Figure 30. Rubble wall composed of roughly dressed boulders local granite and quartzite with pinnings of flaggy black schist, Fort William. BGS © NERC Photo: E. Hyslop.

Figure 31. Church constructed from Precambrian chlorite schist rubble with sandstone dressings, Aberfeldy. BGS © NERC Photo: E. Hyslop.

Slate

The term slate is generally used to describe a thinly laminated stone used for roofing purposes. True slate is a metamorphic rock whose constituent minerals have recrystallized to form cleavage planes along which the stone can easily be split to give a thin 'tile'. Stone slates are thinly bedded sedimentary rocks, which split to produce a suitable tile for roofing purposes. True slate is considered the most appropriate material for roofing, while stone slate may be more porous and can be prone to decay and delamination.

Scotland is very rich in metamorphic rock. Its once large slate industry, based in three areas of the Highlands, includes the West Highland slates from Ballachulish and Easdale; the Highland Border slate belt, incorporating a series of quarries along the north side of the Highland Boundary Fault; and a Northeast slate belt consisting of a series of quarries in Aberdeenshire and Banffshire, dominated by the Foudland quarries near Insch. Detailed accounts of the slate industry and petrographic and physical char-

Stone in Scotland – ISBN 978-92-3-104031-3 – © UNESCO 2006

acteristics of Scottish slate are given in Richey and Anderson (1940) and Walsh (2000). Further details are given in Annex II.

The major areas of slate production were Ballachulish and Easdale, where material was exported by sea to satisfy the demands of late eighteenth and nineteenth century urban development in the Midland Valley of Scotland. The ultimate rise of Welsh slates and man-made materials led to the demise of the industry in the mid-twentieth century. The distinctive presence of pyrite in slate from Ballachulish and Easdale is not a source of decay, as the mineral is typically well crystallized in a stable cubic form, and many of these slates have performed well on buildings for over a century.

Scots slate is distinct in colour and composition from that produced in Wales and England. In addition, the geological complexity of Scottish slate deposits meant that the material was produced in random sizes and variable thickness. Beginning in the nineteenth century, Scots slate was graded into 'sizeable' (approximately 350 × 200 mm), 'undersized' (250 × 150 mm) and 'peggies' (228 × 150 mm), although dimensions varied between different quarries. Slates were traditionally laid in diminishing courses, with the largest at the bottom of the roof and the smallest at the top. These factors give the Scots slate roof a distinctive appearance.

Where the local sedimentary rocks were suitable, stone slates were exploited throughout Scotland. Most of these were quarried for local use, although large quarries were present in some parts of the Southern Uplands (e.g. at Stobo near Peebles). Local varieties of metamorphic rock that could be thinly split, such as schist and amphibolite, were exploited on a small scale throughout the Highlands (e.g. amphibolite on Islay and mica schist near Braemar). Some areas of flagstone production also provided stone slates for roofing (e.g. in Caithness and Angus). The variety of stone types used as roofing slates has led to a rich diversity in roofing materials and roofing styles throughout Scotland. Emerton (2000) describes the regional character of Scottish slated roofs.

West Highland Slate

▶ (i) Ballachulish Quarries, Argyllshire

Ballachulish is the best known of the Scottish slates, both in terms of quantity of production and quality. Quarrying began in the late seventeenth century, rising to a peak in the late nineteenth century, when fifteen million slates were produced annually (Figure 32). The slate is a dark grey colour, typically pyrite-rich, and has a complex geological structure with a distinctive, coarse surface 'grain'. The highest quality Ballachulish slates are between 6 and 9 mm thick, compared to 14 mm or greater for slates in other areas. Ballachulish slate is from the Dalradian Appin Group rocks of Precambrian age (Figure 34).

▶ (ii) Easdale Slate Belt, Argyllshire

Known as the 'Slate Islands', this series of quarries was first recorded in the twelfth century, with major production in the eighteenth century rising to 10 million slates annually by the late nineteenth century. The slate typically has a blue-grey to black colour with common pyrite, and a surface texture varying from smooth to a strong crenulation. Cleavage surfaces are commonly crossed by coarser-grained beds or 'ribboning'. The slate belongs to the Argyll Group Dalradian rocks of Precambrian age. Most of the Easdale quarries are now flooded (Figure 33).

Highland Border Slate Belt

The Highland Border Slate belt extends across Scotland from Arran in the west to Dunkeld in the east. It has been quarried at a large number of locations, both on a small-scale for local use and in larger extraction for export to the main urban centres of Scotland. The main locations of quarries are (from west to east): Arran, Bute, Dunoon, Rosneath, Luss, Aberfoyle, Comrie, Logiealmond and Dunkeld.

The quarries on the west coast, such as in Arran and Bute, supplied slate to Glasgow by sea beginning in the eighteenth century. Transporting slate from the inland quarries was difficult, but inland rivers allowed slate from the Aberfoyle, Perthshire and Luss quarries to reach the Midland Valley from as early as the seventeenth century. Several of these quarries were rejuvenated by railway transport and expanded significantly towards the end of the nineteenth century.

Highland Border slate is from the Southern Highland Group of the Dalradian rocks. It varies considerably in colour, ranging from blue-grey to green and purple; the full range is sometimes found in the same quarry. It is generally smooth with no crenulation or 'grain', although bedding – or 'ribbons' – due to silty bands is common. Pyrite is generally absent. As well as the main quarries mentioned below, many smaller quarries supplied local buildings (Richey and Anderson, 1940; Walsh, 2000; Emerton, 2000).

Slates of northeast Scotland (Aberdeenshire and Banffshire)

There are numerous quarries in this area producing 'Macduff slates' or 'Foudland slate', named after two of the main localities. Production began in the eighteenth century and peaked in the early nineteenth century. Some slates were relatively expensive because of their inland location, and many quarries closed in the second half of the nineteenth century as improved transport connections to other sources created a more competitive market.

The slate is from the Southern Highland Group of the Dalradian rocks. Macduff slates are typically small in size, dark blue-grey or, occasionally, green in colour, with silty beds forming 'ribbons' on cleavage surfaces. Some slates have a spotted texture due to thermal metamorphism from nearby granites.

Stone slate

There are many small quarries throughout Scotland where local stones that are not true slates are capable of being split to produce roofing tiles. Few of these quarries operated on a significant scale and most only served local buildings, although several supplied neighbouring towns and villages.

In the parts of Scotland where flagstone was produced, for example, in Caithness, Orkney and Angus, there is also a tradition of producing stone slate for roofing. Production depends on the ability of the sedimentary rock to split along the thinly separated bedding planes; these stone slates are typically thicker and

heavier than true metamorphic slate (see Flagstone). Certain quarries in these areas specialized in the production of roofing stone (e.g. White Moss and Calder quarries in Caithness and Carmyllie and Haystone quarries in Angus) (Figure 35). Other examples of the local use of thinly bedded, 'flaggy' sedimentary rocks for roofing occur in the Permian and Triassic sandstones of Moray (e.g. in Elgin) and Dumfriesshire.

In the Southern Uplands deformed mudrocks are occasionally fissile enough to be split to produce slate for roofing. Stobo and Grieston quarries near Peebles supplied a dark grey-blue fissile mudstone 'slate' to much of the district from the late seventeenth century. Other quarries were active in the Galloway area in the southwest. In the Highlands higher grade metamorphic rocks such as mica schist and amphibolite are occasionally capable of being split into crude slate tiles, although they also have a mineral composition different from true slate. For example, a number of quarries supplied local schist 'slate' in the Oban area, Islay, Ross of Mull, and throughout Speyside, Tomintoul and the Braemar area.

Figure 32. Khartoum quarry, completed in 1906, one of the Ballachulish slate quarries, produced fifteen million slates annually at the end of the nineteenth century. Photo: A. McKinney.

Stone in Scotland – ISBN 978-92-3-104031-3 – © UNESCO 2006

Figure 33. Abandoned slate quarry now flooded by the sea, Easdale Island. BGS © NERC Photo: E. Hyslop.

Figure 34. Farm building constructed from slate waste and local metamorphic and igneous field boulders, North Ballachulish. BGS © NERC Photo: E. Hyslop.

Figure 35. Stone slates made from Devonian flagstone from the Carmyllie quarries in Angus. Lennoxlove House, East Lothian. BGS © NERC Photo: E. Hyslop.

Figure 36. Outcrops of sandstone and the principal sandstone quarries in Scotland (excluding flagstone). BGS © NERC.

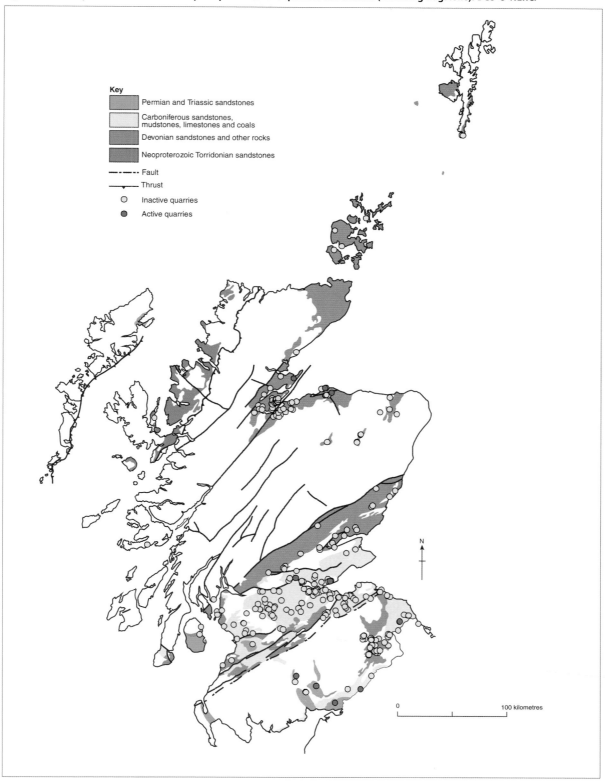

Figure 37. Main outcrops of flagstone-bearing rocks and the principal Scottish flagstone quarries. BGS © NERC.

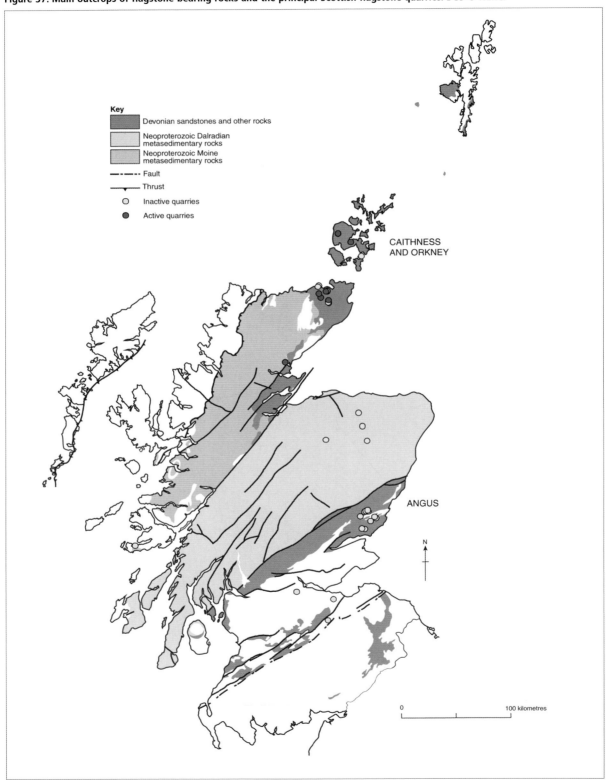

Figure 38. Scottish Limestone and Marble quarries and the major carbonate-bearing outcrops. BGS © NERC.

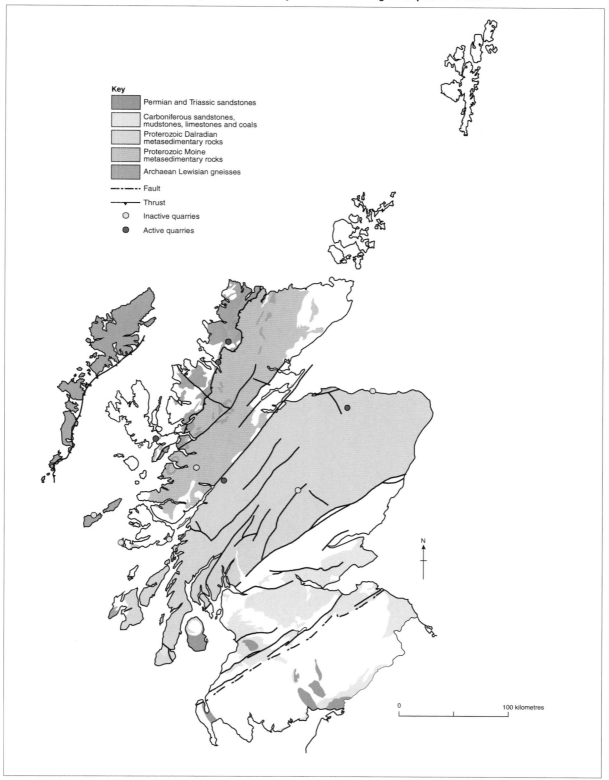

Figure 39. Scottish igneous rock quarries (excluding granite), showing the main rock types. BGS © NERC.

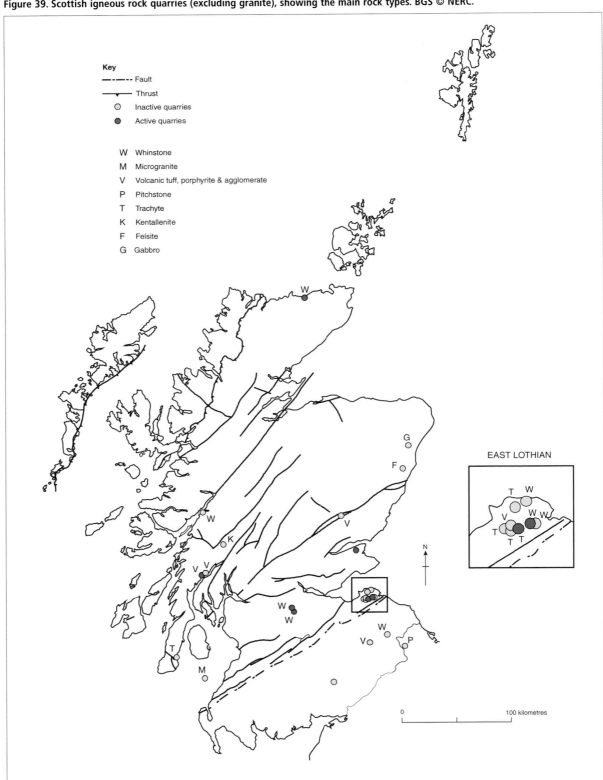

Figure 40. Scottish granite quarries, showing the main granite outcrops. BGS © NERC.

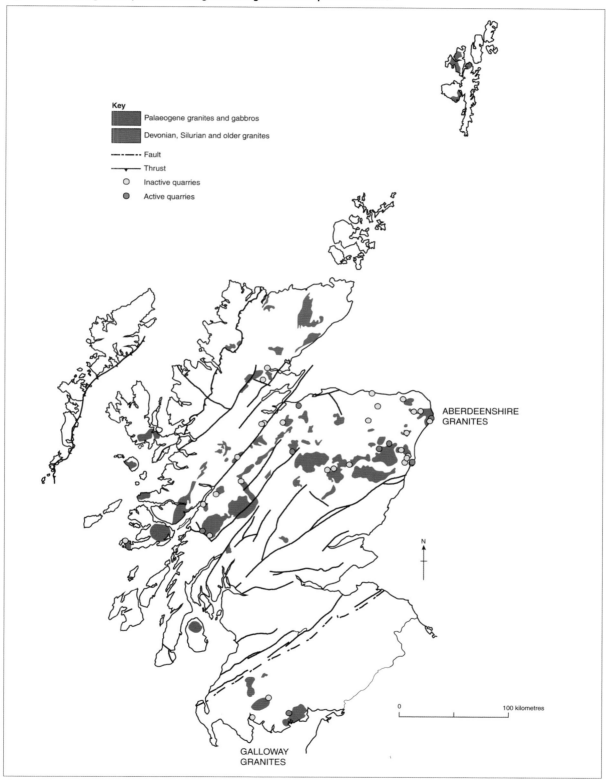

Figure 41. Scottish metamorphic rock quarries (excluding slate), showing the main outcrops of metamorphic rock and quarried rock types.

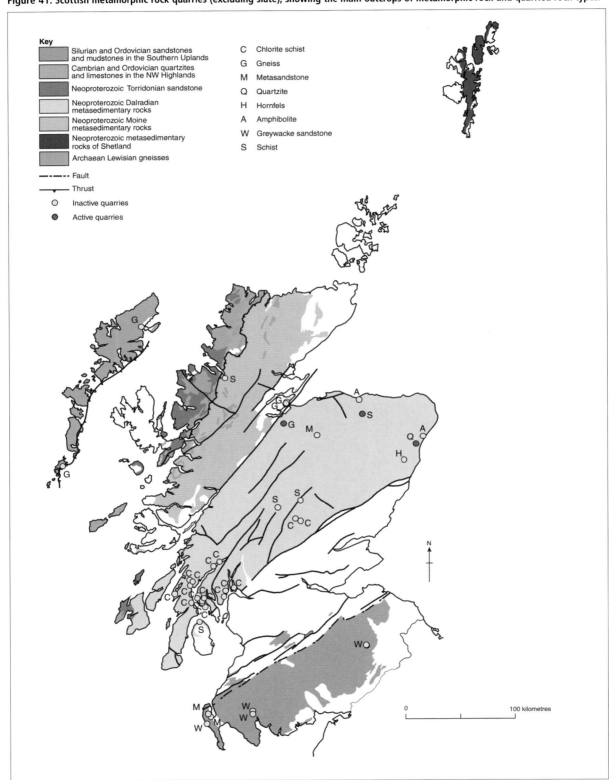

Figure 42. Scottish slate quarries. BGS © NERC.

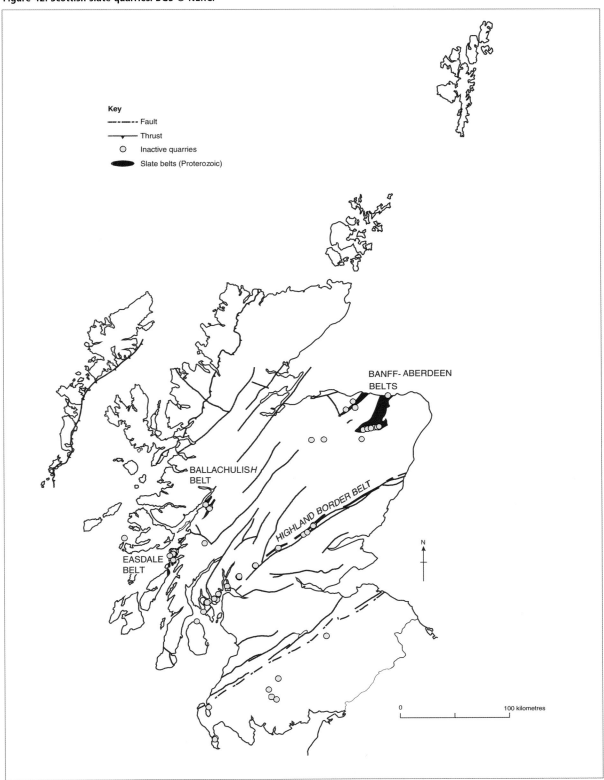

Key
------- Fault
——▾—— Thrust
○   Inactive quarries
⬤   Slate belts (Proterozoic)

BANFF- ABERDEEN
BELTS

BALLACHULISH
BELT

HIGHLAND BORDER BELT

EASDALE
BELT

N

0   100 kilometres

6. Stone technology and skills

For a country that contains significant and varied resources of high quality building stone, the stone industry in Scotland can be described as underdeveloped. Despite the fact that Scotland was a major international stone producer in the nineteenth century, the industry has never recovered from rapid decline during the first half of the twentieth century. The large industrial-scale processing and technological investment seen today in other countries with similar stone resources have not occurred in Scotland. Official statistics show that in the mid-nineteenth century there were 674 registered building stone quarries in Scotland, while today the number is less than twenty-five (data from the British Geological Survey).

Many countries have embarked on government-funded, regional-scale building stone resource surveys. These have largely been undertaken by geological survey organizations whose national geological mapping programmes have allowed them to identify resources for further exploration. Such studies provide a framework within which potential building stone prospects can be investigated on a more detailed scale. In Scotland there is a need for a reassessment of building stone resources on a national scale in order to provide a basis for future development.

6.1 Quarrying

The relatively limited extent of the current building stone extraction industry in Scotland means that many of the modern technological advances seen in other countries, such as diamond wire sawing, have not had a significant impact. With some notable exceptions, most operations are small-scale and depend on a mixture of traditional methods of splitting stone in situ and modern mechanical extraction techniques; the latter require minimal manpower and thereby reduce costs. Although the type and method of extraction vary from place to place, depending on the properties of the particular material, they are often based on traditional working practices. Traditional methods of extraction suit the exploitation of much of Scotland's stone because of the variable and structurally complex geological nature of the reserves.

The building stone industry is different from other extractive stone industries in that it is crucial to maximize the quality and dimensions of the extracted material. Much is dependant upon the experience, skill and knowledge of the particular quarry operator, who can judge where the best stone lies and decide the best way of extracting it with minimum waste. Much use is made of natural planes of weakness, such as joint systems and bedding planes. Overburden is mechanically cleared and the rock surface examined for joint systems. If conditions are favourable, then stone can simply be eased-out using a mechanical 'digger'. Where more massive, the stone is split by drilling a series of regularly-spaced, aligned parallel holes, normally using a hand-held, compressed-air drill, and inducing a fracture using a series of percussive, compressed-air, expansion charges, or by traditional 'plug and feathers' wedges driven into the stone. Inappropriate high velocity explosive blasting can generate microfractures, which reduce the quality of building stone. The use of explosives in building stone extraction is therefore relatively rare, and typically restricted to a traditional black powder charge, which produces a low velocity blast in order to minimize fracturing of the stone.

The use of traditional techniques may appear relatively time-consuming and laborious, but it ensures optimum recovery of good quality, undamaged stone blocks of maximum dimensions. Knowledge and experience of a specific stone type in a quarry help determine such factors as the correct size of wedges and the optimum spacing and orientation of drill holes to suit the particular stone. A highly skilled workforce with local knowledge is invaluable. Today, quarry operators maximize business by also processing less expensive imported stone, while the indigenous material is commonly reserved for a more specialist or prestigious use, which can attract a premium price.

Softer sedimentary rocks and flagstones are commonly extracted by splitting along the natural bedding planes and cutting out large slabs using a mobile circular saw. Blocks are then removed to a cutting shed for more precise machining into required sizes.

6.2 Processing and dressing

Following extraction, blocks are typically removed to a cutting yard for processing (Figure 45). As in other countries, rapid developments in Scotland at the end of the twentieth century have led to the introduction of automated mechanical techniques for stone processing which have revolutionized the industry. Large-scale, mechanized frame saws allow rapid and efficient processing of large stone blocks which can be cut to accurate dimensions (Figure 44). Additional machinery are now widely used for automated surface finishing and profiling, cutting of ornate details and lettering, and especially polishing. Recent increase in demand has led to large-scale investment in specialist equipment, such as in-line computer-controlled production systems used for cutting slate and flagstone in Caithness. Some parts of the industry have invested in systems for the production of cladding panels for new building projects, significantly increasing the potential use of stone for modern construction methods.

The use of mechanized sawing means that most processed stone blocks have smooth sawn faces. It is therefore necessary for a wide range of surface finishing treatments to be available to suit the varying requirements of the market. Natural riven bedding surfaces are commonly retained for flagstone or, more rarely, stone slate. Artificially roughened, flame-textured surfaces created using an oxyacetylene torch have recently been used for granite finishes. Mechanical polishing is now widely applied to different types of stone products, particularly high-value items such as decorative interior surfaces.

Although much dressing or finishing of stone is mechanized, traditional masonry skills are required for specialist and conservation work, where finishes have to be replicated by hand-tooling (Figure 43). The ability to produce traditional masonry surface finishes, such as broaching or droving, point-tooled or stugged, and rock-faced finishes, is essential to maintain the stone built heritage. Such work requires a skilled stone mason, with only minor assistance from modern equipment, such as a mechanized bush-hammer. Some products rely almost entirely on traditional skill, as is the case in the production of flagstone by splitting along a bedding surface to generate a naturally riven surface with the required slip resistance criteria as well as an aesthetically pleasing finish. In general, skilled manual work is important to ensure that a product can be tailored to specific requirements, and to replicate traditional finishes where required.

In order for quarries to be profitable it is important to minimize waste from stone extraction and to diversify into different markets. For example, today quarries can utilize stone that was previously classed as waste by using hydraulic rock guillotines to produce simple, roughly squared blocks for rubble building. In Scotland a number of factors are important in driving such diversification, such as the growth in demand for specific types of indigenous stone for the repair of historic buildings, and an increasing appreciation of the stone built heritage in general. A resurgence of interest in natural stone is reflected in increasing demand for townscape stone paving and kerbs, rubble and dry-stone walling, as well as stone for garden features and interior surfaces. The renewed interest is creating a more attractive economic background for the rebirth of the Scottish stone industry.

An important current issue is the shortage of skilled and qualified (time-served) stone masons. For a country with a significant stone built heritage that requires increasing repair and maintenance, it is imperative that the traditional craft skills involved in the quarrying and dressing of dimension stone are retained. As a result of the decline of the building stone industry during the twentieth century, many of these skills were in danger of being lost. It is only relatively recently that this issue has been recognized and a more coordinated national approach to training, in particular to the apprenticeship schemes, is likely. New skills are also required for the modern use of stone, such as in cladding panels and the laying of paving for streetscapes.

Figure 43. Traditional skilled hand masonry is still much in demand, such as this repair to a church. BGS © NERC Photo: E. Hyslop.

Figure 44. The upper surface of a sandstone bed cleared in order to show the natural joint patterns to maximise the extracted block size. Cullalo quarry, Fife. BGS © NERC Photo: E. Hyslop.

Figure 45. The primary cutting shed of a masonry contractor where large quarried blocks are sawn and loaded onto pallets for further processing. BGS © NERC Photo: E. Hyslop.

7. Environmental and planning issues

Despite increasing market demand for appropriate and indigenous stone, the extraction of Scottish stone is influenced by a number of other factors, some of which can hinder the opening of quarries. One of the main issues is planning policy and legislation. The quarrying of stone is highly regulated by planning legislation, and the reopening of a former quarry or the opening of a new quarry requires compliance with a number of complex procedures before planning permission is granted. This is both a lengthy and expensive process for a potential quarry operator. Because the present-day quarrying industry in Scotland (and the UK) is dominated by the extraction of aggregates, the particular requirements of the dimension stone industry are not always taken into account within the current planning system.

Planning applications require detailed environmental impact assessment studies as well as consideration of transport issues and the effect on surrounding populations. When permission is granted, it is often with strict limitations on the length of time and amount of stone to be extracted, and further permission has to be sought to extend the specified period of extraction. It is particularly difficult to reopen historic quarries that are now close to residential areas. In addition, permission to quarry in areas of outstanding natural beauty, such as in national parks, is controlled by specific legislation. Such restrictions need to take account of the fact that the preservation of the character of an area may be dependant upon maintaining the stone built heritage, which may in turn depend upon continued supplies of local natural stone. Alongside questions of local planning, it should be kept in mind that some historic quarries supplied stone on a national scale. It is important that the planning system take account of

these issues; the quarrying of building stone should be seen as necessary to preserving national heritage and character, as well as to stimulating new economic activity and employment (Figure 46).

A related factor that has significant influence on the planning system is the unfavourable public perception of quarries, whose negative reputation is largely the result of aggregate quarrying. Hard-rock aggregate quarries regularly use explosives and can generate significant noise and dust, and sand and gravel quarries extract and transport very large quantities of material. The presence of industrial-scale aggregate crushing and sorting plants and the very high number and frequency of trucks transporting material results in much public opposition to quarries in general. In addition, the environmental footprint of a modern aggregate quarry is generally very much larger than a building stone quarry. Few people realize that the extraction of dimension stone is a very different procedure, using little if any explosives, and removing and transporting much less material.

Many former quarries are valuable in terms of nature and heritage conservation, education, leisure and tourism, and as such can be viewed as important resources. Former building stone quarries make up a high percentage of sites protected by legislation, as Sites of Special Scientific Interest (SSSI) or as Regionally Important Geological Sites (RIGS). In addition, former quarry sites have been adapted for use as rock climbing centres and for other sport activities. The advantage of such alternative uses is that the quarry is generally retained in its current form without sterilizing the resource; the quarry is perceived as a positive asset to the community.

The presence of large numbers of former building stone quarries in Scotland is an important issue. Local authorities generally have no mechanism for assessing the value of a former quarry, whether it still contains a potential resource or is worked-out. Despite this, they are encouraged to utilize local indigenous sources by national planning guidelines. The need for such assessment should be important when preparing local and regional structure plans, because former quarry sites are commonly seen as potential sites for infilling with waste or for building development. There is a need for a national strategy that creates a mechanism by which an authority or potential quarry operator can assess the potential value of a site as a workable resource, or determine if the geology of adjacent areas is suitable for stone extraction. The current lack of a consistent approach has resulted in several valuable building stone quarries being infilled and effectively sterilized, with the permanent loss of a particular resource. The UK's national and regional commitment to a Strategy on Sustainable Development strengthens the case for the use of indigenous building stones and the reopening of existing former building stone quarries.

Figure 46. Smailholm Tower, Kelso, a fifteenth-century Borders tower house, constructed from local basalt ('whinstone') rubble with dressings of Devonian red sandstone. BGS © NERC Photo: A. McMillan.

Glossary of terms

Only a brief selection of geological, quarrying, architectural and historical terms used in the text are given. For further guidance the following references are recommended:

Walker, P. M. B. (ed.). 1991. *Chambers Earth Science Dictionary*. Edinburgh, W. and R. Chambers.
Pride, G. L. 1996. *Dictionary of Scottish Building*. Edinburgh, The Rutland Press/ Historic Scotland.

Agglomerate (or volcanic breccia) An igneous rock formed mainly from coarse grained fragments of volcanic debris.

Amphibolite Dark-coloured metamorphic rock consisting dominantly of the mineral amphibole.

Andesite Dark, fine grained volcanic rock consisting of feldspar and an iron-magnesium silicate mineral.

Ashlar Hewn or sawn blocks of masonry finely dressed to size and normally laid in regular courses.

Basalt Dark-coloured, fine grained, basic igneous rock consisting of silicate minerals including feldspar, pyroxenes and iron oxides.

Bedding Natural layers formed during deposition of sediments.

Broch Late prehistoric structure consisting of a large round tower with hollow stone-built walls, found mainly in the Highlands and Islands.

Cladding Thin slabs of stone used as external, non-load-bearing covering to building structure.

Conglomerate Sedimentary rock consisting of water-worn pebbles bound together in a sandy matrix.

Corbel Stone or series of stones projecting from a wall used for support.

Course Continuous horizontal layer of stones of uniform height.

Cross-bedding A series of inclined sedimentary bedding planes having a relationship to the direction of current flow (also current-bedding).

Dimension Stone Ashlar or measured stone.

Dip Inclination of strata to the horizontal.

Dolerite Medium-grained basic igneous rock.

Dressed Stone with any kind of worked finish.

Dune Bedding Large-scale cross-bedding typical of windblown sands deposited in desert and beach settings.

Dyke Sheet-like body of igneous rock that cuts across the bedding of the host rock

Fault Fracture in rock along which there has been an observable amount of displacement.

Feldspar The most important single group of rock-forming silicate minerals including silicates of sodium, potassium and calcium.

Felsite A field term for very fine grained igneous rocks, commonly pinkish orange in colour, composed predominantly of quartz and feldspar.

Flagstone Fissile, micaceous, laminated sandstone and siltstone used for paving or roofing.

Freestone Generally a fine grained stone that can be freely worked in any direction, suitable for carving.

Gabbro Coarse crystalline igneous rock consisting of feldspar, pyroxene and sometimes olivine.

Gneiss A coarsely banded crystalline metamorphic rock.

Granite Coarse grained igneous rock consisting of quartz, feldspar and very commonly mica.

Greywacke Fine to coarse grained, hard sandstone consisting of mainly angular rock fragments or quartz grains in a muddy matrix.

Harling Scots term for roughcast, i.e. plaster mixed with small stones used to coat walls

Horonizing The use of slivers of stone placed against each other vertically in the ground to form a tightly fitting stone path, the slivers having been derived during dressing of masonry, typically from the manufacture of basalt or dolerite setts.

Joint A fracture with no displacement. Joints often occur in two sets, more or less vertical and at right angles to each other.

Limekiln Stone-built furnace used for the burning of limestone to form lime for agricultural use or mortar.

Lithology Character of rock in terms of composition, structure and grain size.

Liver Rock A massive sandstone without discernible bedding, which can be worked in all directions (also freestone).

Metamorphic Rock derived by the alteration of pre-existing rocks by action of high temperature and/or pressure in the Earth's crust.

Mica Layered complex hydrated silicate mineral.

Micro- Prefix used to describe an igneous rock of unusually fine grainsize, e.g. microgranite.

Olivine Group of rock-forming, iron and magnesium (ferro-magnesian) silicate minerals.

Pinning(s) Small stone or stones inserted into the void(s) between larger rubble stones to make up the height of a course and tighten the construction.

Porphyrite (or porphyry) An igneous rock containing large crystals within a finer-grained groundmass.

Pyroxene Group of rock-forming, iron and magnesium (ferro-magnesian) silicate minerals.

Quartz Common rock-forming glassy mineral, silica in sedimentary, metamorphic and igneous rocks.

Quoin Stone at external angle of wall, usually bonded with tails extending, alternately, onto both faces.

Random rubble Walling of irregular, unsquared stones not laid in courses.

Ribbons Applied to banded slate, the presence of bedding planes caused by variations of grainsize and composition visible on the cleavage surfaces.

Rubble Uncut stone of variable and irregular shape and size, which was traditionally laid in rough courses.

Sandstone Sedimentary rock composed of detrital sand grains naturally cemented. Sandstones vary widely in composition and can be classified according to grain mineralogy. A sandstone with high clay content may be referred to as argillaceous.

Schist A finely layered metamorphic rock that splits easily into parallel layers.

Sett Stone roughly squared for paving.

Sill A sheet of igneous rock intruded along the bedding planes of pre-existing rocks.

Smithy A blacksmith's forge for the working of iron and other metals.

Squared rubble Irregularly formed stones, roughly worked to a more consistent shape so that they can be built more readily into courses.

Tooled Dressed stone with hewing mason's tool marks evident on the surface. A wide range of textures can be produced.

Trachyte Generally pale-coloured igneous rock composed of large crystals in a fine grained glassy groundmass.

Tuff Igneous rock formed mainly from indurated fine grained volcanic ash.

Whinstone Colloquial term for any hard, dark stone in Scotland and the north of England, although geologically restricted to dark compact igneous rocks such as basalt or dolerite.

Stone in Scotland – ISBN 978-92-3-104031-3 – © UNESCO 2006

References and further reading

Anderson, J. G. C. 1939. The granites of Scotland. Special Report of the mineral resources of Great Britain, Vol. 32. *Memoirs of the Geological Survey of Great Britain*. Edinburgh, HMSO.

Bartlam, W. A. 2001. *Stones and Quarrying in Moray*. Elgin, UK, W. Ashley Bartlam.

British Geological Survey. 2001. *Building Stone Resources Map of Britain*. Nottingham, UK, British Geological Survey.

Brown, J. (ed.). 2002. *Flagstone Village: Castletown, Caithness*. Castletown, UK, Castletown Heritage.

Cameron, D. G. et al. 2005. *Directory of Mines and Quarries 2003*. Nottingham, UK, British Geological Survey.

Davey, A., Heath, B., Hodges, D., Ketchin M. and Milne, R. 1995. *The Care and Conservation of Georgian Houses*. Oxford, UK, Butterworth Heinemann.

Diack, W. 1941. Rise and Progress of the Granite Industry of Aberdeen. *The Quarry Managers' Journal*, April 1941–February 1942.

Elsden, J. V. and Howe, J. A. 1923. *The Stones of London: A Descriptive Guide to the Principal Stones Used in London*. London, Colliery Guardian Co.

Emerton, G. 2000. *The Pattern of Scottish Roofing*. Edinburgh, UK, Historic Scotland.

Glasgow Conservation Trust West. 1993–1999. Chapter 3: Stonework. *West End Conservation Manual*. Glasgow, UK, Glasgow Conservation Trust West.

Hawkins, J. I. 2001. *The Sandstone Heritage of Dumfriesshire*. Dumfries, UK, The Friends of Annandale and Eskdale Museums.

Hunt, R. 1859. Part 1. Memoir of the Geological Survey of Great Britain. *Mineral Statistics of the United Kingdom of Great Britain and Ireland for the year 1858*. London, Geological Survey of Great Britain.

Hutton + Rostron. Historic Scotland. 1997. *Research Report: A Future for Stone in Scotland*. Edinburgh, UK, Historic Scotland.

Hyslop, E. K. 2004. *Research Report: The Performance of Replacement Sandstone in the New Town of Edinburgh*. Edinburgh, UK, Historic Scotland.

Hyslop, E. K. and McMillan, A. A. 2003. *A Pilot Study into the Potential for a Building Stones of Scotland Publication*. Reference Report, Edinburgh, UK, Historic Scotland.

Jeffrey, A. 1855–64. *The History and Antiquities of Roxburghshire and Adjoining Districts*. Edinburgh, UK, Vol. i–iii, T. C. Jack/Vol. iv, Seton and Mackenzie.

Lawson, J. 1981. *Building Stones of Glasgow*. Glasgow, UK, Geological Society of Glasgow.

Lawson, J. 2000. Introduction: Geology, Walker, F. A. (ed.), *Argyll and Bute. The Buildings of Scotland*. London, Penguin Books, in association with Buildings of Scotland Trust.

Leary, E. 1986. The building sandstones of the British Isles. *Building Research Establishment Report*. London, HMSO.

MacGregor, A. G. 1945. The mineral resources of the Lothians. *Wartime Pamphlet,* No. 45. London, Geological Survey of Great Britain.

MacGregor, A. G. and Eckford, R. J. A. 1946. The Upper Old Red and Lower Carboniferous sediments of Teviotdale and Tweedside, and the stones of the abbeys of the Scottish Borderland. *Transactions of the Edinburgh Geological Society*, No. 14, pp. 230–252.

Mackie, A. 1980. Sandstone quarrying in Angus – some thoughts on an old craft. *The Edinburgh Geologist*, No. 8, pp. 14–25.

MacLeod, G. S. and Fenn, R. W. D. 1999. The Dalbeattie granite industry. *Tarmac Papers – The Archives and History Initiative of Tarmac*, No. 3, pp. 219–261.

Maxwell, I. 1992. Stone: the changing perception of traditional build in materials and traditions in Scottish building. Riches, A. and Stell, G. (eds), *Regional and Thematic Studies*, No. 2. Edinburgh, UK, Scottish Vernacular Buildings Working Group.

Maxwell, I. 1996. *Building Materials of the Scottish Farmstead*. Edinburgh, UK, Scottish Vernacular Buildings Working Group.

McMillan, A. A. 1997. Quarries of Scotland: an illustrated guide to Scottish geology and stone working based on the British Geological Survey photographic archive of selected building stone quarries. *Historic Scotland Technical Advice Note*, No. 12. Edinburgh, UK, Historic Scotland.

McMillan, A. A. 2006. Topography and building materials. Cruft, K., Dunbar, J. and Fawcett, R. (eds), *The Buildings of Scotland: Borders*. London, Yale University Press, in association with the Buildings of Scotland Trust.

McMillan, A. A., Gillanders, R. J. and Fairhurst, J. A. 1999. *Building Stones of Edinburgh*. Edinburgh, UK, Edinburgh Geological Society.

Natural Stone Directory, No. 14, 2004–5. Nottingham, UK, QMJ Publishing.

Oosterhuis, W. R. (ed.). 1999. *Stone in Southern Africa*. Paris, UNESCO Publishing/Faenza, Italy, Gruppo Editoritale Faenza Editrice.

Richey, J. E. and Anderson, J. G. C. 1940. *Scottish Slates. Wartime Pamphlet*, No. 40. London, Geological Survey of Great Britain.

Robertson, T., Simpson, J. B. and Anderson, J. G. C. 1949. *The limestones of Scotland. Special reports on the mineral resources of Great Britain*, No. 35. Edinburgh, UK, HMSO.

Selonen, O. and Suominen, V. (eds). 2003. *Nordic Stone*. Paris, UNESCO Publishing/IAEG.

Shadmon, A. 1993. Dimension Stone – its impact on environmental and constructional implications. *IAEG Bulletin*, No. 48, pp. 119–122.

Shadmon, A. 2005. Stone Absolute (By any other name). *LITOS*, No. 78.

Wilson, P. (ed.). 2005. *Building with Scottish Stone*. Edinburgh, UK, Arcamedia for Natural Stone Institute.

Walsh, J. A. 2000. Scottish slate quarries. *Historic Scotland Technical Advice Note*, No. 21. Edinburgh, UK, Historic Scotland.

Watson, J. 1911. *British and Foreign Building Stones: A Descriptive Catalogue of the Specimens in the Sedgwick Museum, Cambridge*. Cambridge, UK, Cambridge University Press.

Further detailed information is contained in memoirs, sheet descriptions, special reports and enquiry records of the British Geological Survey. Some information on building stones is also given in the Buildings of Scotland Series (Pevsner Architectural Guides).

Annex I

Atlas and properties of selected Scottish building stones

Atlas of selected Scottish building stones

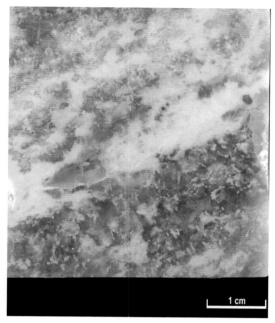

Iona marble, Argyllshire (Precambrian). Polished surface.
BGS © NERC.

Corrennie granite, Aberdeenshire (Silurian). Polished surface.
BGS © NERC.

Furnace porphyrite, Argyllshire (Devonian/Silurian). Polished surface. BGS © NERC.

West Highland slate (Precambrian). Natural riven surface.
BGS © NERC.

Swinton sandstone, Berwickshire (Carboniferous). Natural surface BGS © NERC.

Cullalo sandstone, Fife (Carboniferous). Natural surface.
BGS © NERC.

Tiree marble, West Highlands (Precambrian) Polished surface. BGS © NERC.

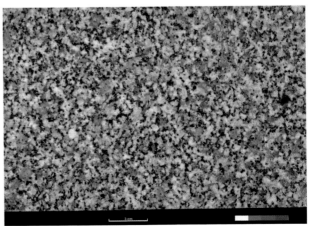

Criffel-Dalbeattie granite, Galloway (Silurian). Polished surface. BGS © NERC.

Corsehill sandstone, Dumfries and Galloway (Triassic). Natural surface. BGS © NERC.

Locharbriggs sandstone, Dumfries and Galloway (Permian). Natural surface. BGS © NERC.

Caithness flagstone, Highlands (Devonian). Natural riven surface. BGS © NERC.

Clashach sandstone, Moray (Permian). Natural surface. BGS © NERC.

Properties of selected Scottish building stones

Table 2: Comparative table of data*

Quarry	Commercial name	Rock Type	Mass Density (kg/m³)	Water absorption (weight %)	Porosity (%)	Compression Strength (MPa)
Binny		Sandstone	2175	11.2	16.2	
Calder	Calder Stone	Flagstone	2710	0.05	2	
Clashach	Clashach coloured	Sandstone	2007	17.1	22.5	
Clashach	Clashach Standard	Sandstone	2346	5.2	9.2	
Clashach	Clashach sandstone	Sandstone	2084	6.9	21.4	132.3
Corncockle		Sandstone	2130	13.1	18.8	
Corncockle		Sandstone	2170	5.7	19.5	72.5
Corrennie	Corrennie Pink	Granite		0.6		
Corsehill		Sandstone	1990	14.8	22	
Corsehill		Sandstone	1888	10.1	28.8	67.6
Cove	Cove Red	Sandstone	2034	11.5	23	56.2
Craigleith		Sandstone	2220	6.8	13.5	
Craigmillar		Sandstone	2350	8	9.2	
Cullalo		Sandstone	2160	11.2	18.4	
Dunmore (new)		Sandstone			17.3	
Gatelawbridge		Sandstone	2037	15.8	22.6	
Grange		Sandstone	2120	15.1	19.5	
Hailes		Sandstone	2223	10.9	14.5	
Hawkhill Wood		Sandstone	2370	7.1	10.1	
Hermand		Sandstone	2210	11.2	15.1	
Kemnay		Granite	2590	0.7		
Locharbriggs		Sandstone	2210	11.2	15.1	
Locharbriggs		Sandstone	2173	5.7	18.2-24.9	47.3
Newbigging		Sandstone	2130	12.6	18.9	
Plean		Sandstone	2180	14.4	17.7	
Ravelston		Sandstone	2630	2.6	3.6	
Ravelston No.2		Sandstone	2280	8.3	13.8	
Spittal No. 1	Caithness Flagstone	Flagstone	2700	0.4	0.5	
Spittal No. 2	Caithness Flagstone	Flagstone	2648	0.1	0.3	
Spynie		Sandstone	2070	12.2	17.9	
Spynie		Sandstone	2290	3.1	13.3	62.1

(*Note: the authors and publisher take no responsability for the accuracy of this information, which has been compiled from a number of sources)

Flexural strength (MPa)	Point-load Strength (MN/m²)	Saturated sodium sulphate test		Acid resistance u = unaffected; c = colour affected v = variable results	Source of data
		cycles	% loss		
	1.1	10	100	c	McMillan et al. (1999)
22.3			0	Pass	Natural Stone Directory 2004-5/IBIS
	1.9	15	17	u	McMillan et al. (1999)
	9	15	0	u	McMillan et al. (1999)
7.6			0	u	BRE/British Stone List.
	0.8	8	100	c	McMillan et al. (1999)
6.9			2.52	Pass	BRE/ British Stonelist
					Aggregate Industries UK Ltd.
	1.9	15	24	c	McMillan et al. (1999)
5.7			92	u	BRE/British Stone List
8.52				Pass	Block Stone Ltd
		15	30	u	Davey et al. (1978); McMillan et al. (1999)
	3.2	12	100	v	McMillan et al. (1999)
	2.6	15	15	u	McMillan et al. (1999)
		15	23		Leary (1986), McMillan et al. (1999)
	1.7	8	100	c	McMillan et al. (1999)
	0.7	15	57	u	McMillan et al. (1999)
		15	15	u	McMillan et al. (1999)
	3	15	8	v	McMillan et al. (1999)
	2	15	100	u	McMillan et al. (1999)
					Aggregate Industries UK Ltd.
	1.5	15	100	u	McMillan et al. (1999)
5.1			51	u	BRE/British Stone list
	0.6	10	100	v	McMillan et al. (1999)
	1.3	6	100	u	McMillan et al. (1999)
	3.8	15	0	v	McMillan et al. (1999)
	3.1	15	11	c	McMillan et al. (1999)
	16.2	15	0	u	McMillan et al. (1999)
37.2			0.05	v	BRE/British Stone List
	3.8	15	6	u	McMillan et al. (1999)
9.4			18	v	BRE/British Stone List

Annex II

Case studies of current issues: Edinburgh sandstone and Scottish slate

Case study 1: Problems of source and supply of sandstone for conservation in the Edinburgh World Heritage Site

By Ewan Hyslop

As the capital of Scotland, the city of Edinburgh is a centre of political, financial and cultural activity where tourism and heritage are of particular importance. The New Town of Edinburgh was constructed in the eighteenth and nineteenth centuries using local sandstone from quarries in and around the city. It is acknowledged as one of the foremost examples of urban design in Europe and forms part of a UNESCO World Heritage Site. By the end of the twentieth century, all the original quarries had closed and stone for repairs was imported from other parts of the UK. Examination of petrological characteristics indicates that there are marked differences between the original and replacement stone types. These differences have an effect on the visual appearance of repairs, but more importantly may cause accelerated decay of the historic masonry.

Original quarry sources

The rapid development of Edinburgh in the late eighteenth century created a great demand for high quality sandstone, which was obtained from a number of local quarries within a few kilometres' distance of the centre of the city (McMillan et al., 1999). The principal source of sandstone was Craigleith Quarry on the city outskirts, which began operating in the seventeenth century and continued production over a period of about 300 years. The quality of the sandstone was such that the material earned a worldwide reputation and was exported to London and overseas.

Over time, improved transport systems allowed stone to be obtained from further afield, initially by sea, then by canal from the western part of the Midland Valley, and finally by the railway network. By the early twentieth century most of the local quarries had closed, and those remaining were much reduced in output.

Sources of replacement stone for repairs

Today none of the original sandstone quarries that supplied stone for the construction of the Edinburgh New Town are operating, and all the stone has to be imported from other parts of the UK. At least 14 different quarry sources of replacement of sandstone are currently used, and over 85% of the stone is Carboniferous sandstone from the north of England.

The replacement sandstones are generally excellent building stones with proven records of performance over hundreds of years in their local areas, and comparison of geotechnical and other test results suggests that there is a general similarity between the physical properties of the replacement and original stone types (McMillan et al., 1999; Davey et al., 1995). However, test results are indicative of the properties of a stone type, rather than of performance in a particular building. Where replacement stone has to be placed alongside historic masonry, issues of compatibility must also be considered. For example, a replacement stone type that is significantly 'harder' or more 'durable' than the original masonry could reduce the life of the surrounding original masonry in a historic building (Hyslop, 2004).

Stone in Scotland – ISBN 978-92-3-104031-3 – © UNESCO 2006

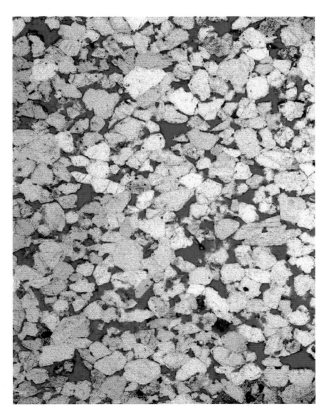

Photo 1. Thin section microscope image of sandstone from Craigleith quarry in Edinburgh, the principal stone type typical of the local stone used in the construction of the Edinburgh New Town. Porosity is highlighted by blue dye resin.
(Image c. 3 mm across.) Photo: E. Hyslop.

Photo 2. Thin section image of sandstone from northern England currently used for the repair of buildings in Edinburgh, showing different characteristics of composition, grainsize and porosity compared to Craigleith sandstone.
(Image c. 3 mm across.) Photo: E. Hyslop.

Petrological comparison of original and replacement sandstones

Comparison of replacement sandstone types used for repair with the original sandstone types examined a number of criteria, including mineral composition, grainsize, sorting characteristics, cementation, porosity and texture. Overall, the original sandstone types have a restricted range of yellowish-grey colour with a uniform, well-sorted and fine grainsize. In contrast, the replacement sandstone types are more variable, with more pale, greyish-orange colours related to the presence of iron oxides, and with typically more variable and coarser grainsizes.

In thin section the original Edinburgh sandstones are dominated by quartz with minor feldspar and have a very open pore structure and strong silica cement (Photo 1). Replacement sandstones have a distinct character with a variable mineral composition typically containing more feldspar, mica and iron oxides (Photo 2). Common fine grained clay minerals and secondary iron oxides result in more restricted porosity characteristics.

Performance of replacement sandstone in buildings

Examination of masonry repairs shows that the petrological differences become apparent in a number of ways. Although replacement stone generally has a stronger colour than the historic masonry, this is obscured by discoloration of the original masonry by soiling, weathering and stonecleaning. Replacement stone with a different texture, grainsize and porosity may be finished or tooled differently from the original masonry. For example, the use of a poorly sorted, coarser-grained sandstone to replace an original fine grained uniform sandstone is obvious, as the replacement stone will not allow the mason to give the same finely tooled finish as the original stone.

The positioning of replacement sandstone immediately adjacent to historic masonry with different petrological characteristics has led to accelerated decay of the original historic stone where the replacement stone is more compact with a restricted pore structure, thus making it more resistant to the processes of weathering and decay (Hyslop, 2004). Acceleration of decay is observed where the original masonry appears to be undergoing rapid deterioration immediately adjacent to replacement sandstone.

Conclusions

Microscopic examination of replacement sandstones currently used for repairing historic buildings in Edinburgh's New Town shows significant differences with the historic masonry used in the original construction of the buildings. Observations of accelerated decay in the historic masonry adjacent to new stone repairs raise concern over the long-term compatibility of using such different stone types together in a building. In order to prevent such damage occurring, it is essential to select a replacement sandstone that has similar petrological characteristics to the original. This is currently made difficult by the limited number of quarry sources available and by the lack of sources of stone in the Edinburgh area. This highlights the need for a national resource assessment to examine abandoned sandstone quarries and the potential for new sources of building stone where appropriate sandstone types can be 'fingerprinted'. The situation described here for the Edinburgh New Town typifies the problems in obtaining replacement sandstone throughout Scotland, where original sources of stone are not available and there is a need to reopen former quarries or open new quarries in appropriate stone.

Case study 2: Identification and future supply of Scottish slate

By Joan Walsh

Slate quarrying was one of Scotland's most significant building stone industries from the eighteenth to the early twentieth centuries. The importance of indigenous slate to the built heritage has long been recognized; the indigenous slate gives a characteristic appearance to traditional Scottish buildings and townscapes. Although slates from different parts of Scotland have different characteristics, there is a particular aesthetic to a Scots slate roof, which results from the typically dark colour, rough texture and variable size of the slates. The use of diminishing courses, with the largest slates at the base of the roof and the smallest at the top, is almost ubiquitous. These factors combine to give a unique and almost organic appearance to traditional Scottish slate roofs.

There are four main types of Scottish slate (i.e. true metamorphic slate): Ballachulish, Easdale, Highland Boundary and Macduff – or 'Northeast'. Slate from each of these areas has its own characteristics and weathering properties.

Scottish roofing slates are still found on the roofs of traditional buildings throughout Scotland. The distribution of the different types of slate can be related to both geographical location (geology) and the history of the industry. At the height of production in the late nineteenth century, Ballachulish quarries produced 15 million slates annually, which coincided with the rapid growth of the main towns and cities in Scotland. Ballachulish slates are still found extensively in conservation areas in Edinburgh and Glasgow and throughout Scotland. The material has become synonymous with Scottish slate.

In the eighteenth century Easdale slate was the best known, being transported by sea throughout Scotland (mainly to the east coast) and exported as far as Australia. Although superseded by Ballachulish in the nineteenth century as the main producer of Scottish slate, Easdale slates continued to be produced until the 1960s.

Highland Boundary slate was mostly produced from small quarries for local use. However, Aberfoyle slate quarries operated on a larger scale and survived into the twentieth century. These slates are found on houses built in the 1930s in the Central Belt.

In the early nineteenth century, production of Macduff slates in the northeast of Scotland was increasing. For example, Foudland Quarry, the largest of the Macduff quarries, maintained an annual production of 800,000 for 30 years. Distribution of Macduff slate is confined to Aberdeenshire and Banffshire.

There are many other examples of slate being quarried on a small scale and used locally. In some cases an estate quarry supplied a castle and surrounding buildings.

The demise of the Scottish industry and the selection of suitable replacements

The Scottish slate industry was severely affected by the expansion of the railway system in the second half of the nineteenth century, which facilitated the transport of cheaper Welsh (and other) slates. In addition, the shortage of manpower during the First and Second World Wars also contributed to the demise of the industry. Production dwindled through the first half of the twentieth century, and ceased by the 1960s.

Today, repairs and maintenance rely on second-hand slates or imported alternatives. This has resulted in many slate roofs being patched with incompatible slates, which is unsightly. Other traditional slate roofs have been replaced by concrete and clay tile, and many urban roofs, once covered with the same slate, are now a patchwork of different types of material, irreversibly changing the harmonious appearance. Many replacement slates are finer grained with higher clay contents and a shorter service life than the original, and failure within a few years of exposure on a roof is not uncommon.

Replacement slates should be selected that have a similar texture and weathering behaviour to the original. This is best achieved by matching as closely as possible the chemical and physical properties of the existing slates. The first step in all repairs and maintenance should be the identification of the original slate, to enable the selection of suitable material for replacement.

Scientific fingerprinting of Scottish slate

The principal minerals present in slate are quartz and the phyllosilicates, white mica and chlorite. These are found in approximately the same proportions regardless of source, and are of limited use in identifying the provenance. Instead, it is necessary to look at the variation in the type and concentration of accessory minerals present, which depend on the environment of deposition of the original silt or mud deposit. For example, haematite is found in Macduff and Highland Boundary slates but not in Ballachulish and Easdale. Both Ballachulish and Easdale contain pyrite, and the size and distribution can be related to quarry source. The chemical composition of the phyllosilicates can also be used for identification. For example, the type of white mica varies from illite to muscovite and to their sodium-rich equivalents, brammallite and paragonite, which can be related to source.

No single property uniquely identifies the slate; instead, a combination of mineralogy, fabric and chemical composition is used. Research is currently underway to database characteristics of slates from all the slate quarries in Scotland in order to aid identification of sources and select appropriate replacements. Some of the main criteria used for fingerprinting are given below.

Visual examination is used to identify colour, grain size, mineral lineation, bedding features and larger grains such as pyrite. The type of pyrite present and a strong mineral lineation are key properties in identifying Ballachulish slate (Photo 3). Crenulation cleavage is commonly found in Easdale slate, and the angle the crenulation makes with the mineral lineation can be related to a subgroup of quarries. Highland Boundary slate comes in a range of colours often characterized by bedding features called 'ribboning'. Dark specks, due to the presence of altered biotite grains, are visible in Macduff slates.

X-ray diffraction (XRD) analysis is used to identify the minerals present and their approximate proportions, and is the simplest method of distinguishing between polymorphs of the same minerals, such as anatase and rutile. It also identifies the type of carbonate present: dolomite, aragonite, or magnesite, which may be related to source; for example, dolomite is present in some Ballachulish slates. The types of feldspar present are a feature used to distinguish between Scottish and replacement Spanish slates. XRD analysis is also used to measure crystallinity, a key factor in determining the durability of a slate. The position of the white mica peak is used to distinguish between Welsh grey and Scottish slate.

Optical and scanning electron microscopes are used to identify minerals present in very small concentrations, such as chloritoid, zircon, monazite, apatite, among others. The assemblages of iron ore minerals present are a key feature in identifying the environment of deposition of the original mudstones and hence the provenance of the slate.

Total oxide analysis using x-ray fluorescence is of limited use in finger-printing slates, although trace element analysis is potentially of great use. Research is being carried out to determine the natural variation in the concentration of the trace elements at source in order to identify those elements that can relate a slate to that source.

Resource assessment

Research is underway to identify a new source of Scottish slate. All the former quarries have been re-surveyed and two quarries identified as suitable for further testing, at Khartoum (Ballachulish) and the Hill of Foudland (Macduff). Slates extracted from these quarries have now been tested to recognized standards. Some of the key features are described below.

Ballachulish slate from Khartoum quarry

Khartoum slate is grey-black with a slight sheen. It is coarse-grained, giving the slate a gritty texture. One of the most distinctive characteristics of this type of slate is the strong mineral lineation clearly visible on the surface. Pyrite grains are common and are usually widely dispersed throughout the slate. The smaller grains are

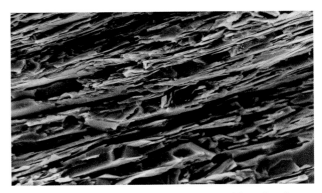

Photo 3. Ballachulish slates have a strong mineral lineation due to the stretching of individual grains of quartz. Image is c. 150 microns across. Micrograph: J. Walsh.

subeuhedral, which means that they have recognizable but imperfect crystal faces; the larger grains have irregular faces and thus are anhedral. In addition, there are large clusters of pyrite grains concentrated in quartz veins running through the blocks of slate. The slate is very durable due to the higher than average metamorphic grade and the coarseness of the quartz grains. Pyrite grains are present in euhedral form, making them less vulnerable to weathering.

Macduff slate from the Hill of Foudland

The slate is blue-grey in colour with a rough gritty texture. It is possible to see small grains of quartz on the surface. The most distinctive property of Macduff slate is 'spotting': small dark specks approximately 0.5 mm in size, evenly distributed throughout the slate. These dark spots are mainly chlorite with mica intergrowths along the cleavage. Accessory minerals are haematite, chloritoid, anatase, zircon and apatite. The presence of haematite, indicative of a fairly oxidized mineral assemblage, makes the slate very durable, with a life expectancy of over 150 years. It becomes slightly paler after exposure on a roof.

Conclusions

Mineralogical and geochemical analysis is being undertaken in order to identify the properties of traditional Scottish slate types from former quarry sources across the country. This will result in a large database, which can be used for the identification of appropriate materials for repair and replacement of traditional Scottish roofs, whether by imported slate or by the reopening of former quarries.

Index of quarries and stone-producing districts

Stone in Scotland – ISBN 978-92-3-104031-3 – © UNESCO 2006